Expeditions
in Reading

5

K12 Summit
CURRICULUM

Book Staff and Contributors

Kristen Kinney-Haines   *Director, English Language Arts*
Amy Rauen   *Director, Instructional Design*
Charlotte Fullerton   *Senior Media Editor*
Mary Beck Desmond   *Senior Text Editor*
Tricia Battipede   *Senior Creative Manager, Cover Design*
Caitlin Gildrien   *Print Visual Designer, Cover Design*
Tim Mansfield   *Writer*
DoubleInk Publishing Services   *Print Visual Design*

About K12 Inc.

K12 Inc. (NYSE: LRN) drives innovation and advances the quality of education by delivering state-of-the-art digital learning platforms and technology to students and school districts around the world. K12 is a company of educators offering its online and blended curriculum to charter schools, public school districts, private schools, and directly to families. More information can be found at K12.com.

Illustrations Credits

All illustrations © K12 unless otherwise noted
37, 45 Jim Starr. **110, 115, 121, 127, 130, 139, 142** Lisa Webber.

Photo Credits

Front Cover   Island © Salamahin/Shutterstock; Dolphin © mixxx83/iStock.
Cover and Interior Pattern   Spiral © Silmen/iStock
Title Page   Dolphin © mixxx83/iStock
8 Katherine Johnson NASA. **11** Mercury Redstone 3 NASA. **13** President Barack Obama presents Katherine G Johnson with the Presidential Medal of Freedom © Kris Connor/WireImage/Getty Images. **15** Katherine Johnson NASA. **16** Mary Jackson NASA. **19** NACA staff NASA. **20** Mary Jackson NASA Langley Research Center. **22** Dorothy Johnson Vaughan © The Picture Art Collection/Alamy Stock Photo. **25** NASA staff © Smith Collection/Gado/Getty Images. **27** Tahani Amer NASA. **28** Debbie Martinez NASA. **32** Julie Williams Byrd NASA. **47** Kate Shelley and mother © Max Ginsberg Studio. **48** Kate Shelley holding pigs © Max Ginsberg Studio. **50** Kate Shelley holding lantern © Max Ginsberg Studio. **53** Train Library of Congress, Prints and Photographs Division, LC-USZC2-2926. **54** Young Frederick Douglass The Granger Collection, New York. 55 Frame © belterz/iStock; Frederick Douglass ©Bettmann/Getty Images. **62** Frederick Douglass ©wynnter/Getty Images. **65** Clara Barton ©Print Collector/Getty Images; Frame © Ivaylo Ivanov/Shutterstock. **67** Clara Barton on the battlefield © The Granger Collection, New York. **71** Clara Barton National Historic Site/National Park Service. **77** Laser pointer © Jiripravda/Shutterstock. **78** Butterfly © tahir abbas/iStock; Monarch butterfly wing © BrianLasenby/iStock; Smart phone © hanibaram/iStock. **80** Laboratory © Anawat_s/iStock. **87** Solar panels with technician © zstockphotos/iStock. **89** Skyscrapers of downtown Los Angeles in haze ©imageBROKER/Alamy Stock Photo. **91** Solar panels in Death Valley National Park ©Wiskerke/Alamy Stock Photo. **95** Solar panels © WangAnQi/iStock. **97** Sunset with electrical power lines © KGrif/iStock. **102** Supreme Court nominee Judge Sonia Sotomayor © Nicholas Kamm/AFP/Getty Images. **105** Gavel © Nastco/iStock.

978-1-60153-572-6

Printed by Walsworth, Marceline, MO, USA, April 2019

Expeditions
in Reading

K12 Summit
CURRICULUM

Table of Contents

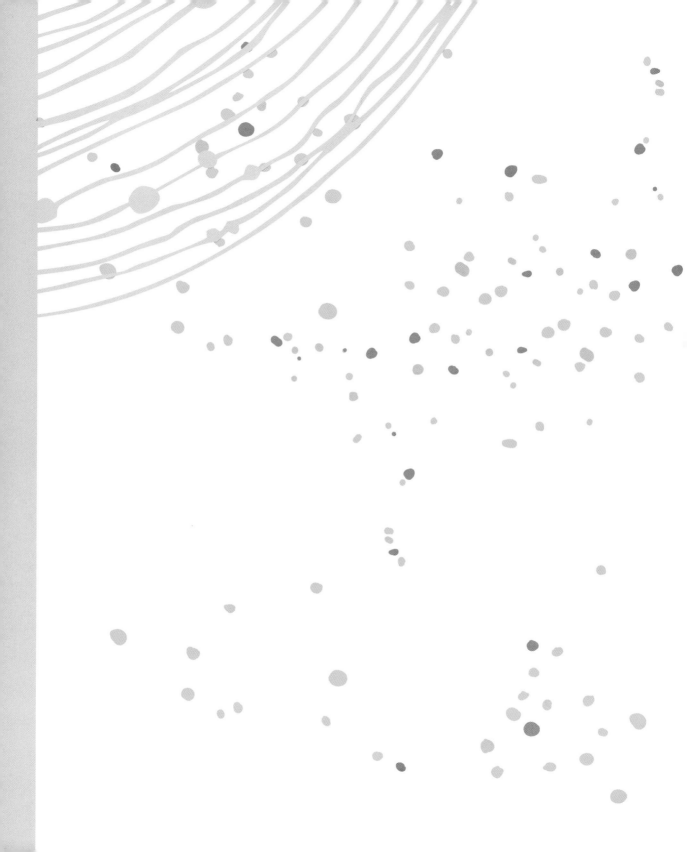

Hidden Figures

Katherine Johnson Biography

by Margot Lee Shetterly for NASA.gov

Date of Birth: August 26, 1918
Hometown: White Sulphur Springs, West Virginia
Education: B.S., Mathematics and French, West Virginia State College, 1937
Hired by NACA: June 1953
Retired from NASA: 1986
Actress Playing Role in *Hidden Figures:* Taraji P. Henson

Being handpicked to be one of three black students to integrate West Virginia's graduate schools is something that many people would consider one of their life's most notable moments, but it's just one of several breakthroughs that have marked Katherine Johnson's long and remarkable life. Born in White Sulphur Springs, West Virginia in 1918, Katherine Johnson's intense curiosity and brilliance with numbers vaulted her ahead several grades in school. By thirteen, she was attending the high school on the campus of historically black West Virginia State College. At eighteen, she enrolled in the college itself, where she made quick work of the school's math curriculum and found a **mentor** in math professor W.W. Schieffelin Claytor, the third African American to earn a Ph.D. in Mathematics. Katherine graduated with highest honors in 1937 and took a job teaching at a black public school in Virginia.

When West Virginia decided to quietly **integrate** its graduate schools in 1939, West Virginia State's president Dr. John W. Davis selected Katherine and two male students as the first black students to be offered spots at the state's flagship school, West Virginia University. Katherine left her teaching job and enrolled in the graduate math program. At the end of the first session, however, she decided to leave school to start a family with her husband. She returned to teaching when her three daughters got older, but it wasn't until 1952 that a relative told her about open positions at the all-black West Area Computing section at the National Advisory Committee

mentor a trusted guide, tutor, or coach
integrate to blend or unite; in this context, to bring a group, such as African American citizens, into equal membership in an organization, such as a university

for Aeronautics (NACA) Langley laboratory, headed by fellow West Virginian Dorothy Vaughan. Katherine and her husband, James Goble, decided to move the family to Newport News to pursue the opportunity, and Katherine began work at Langley in the summer of 1953. Just two weeks into Katherine's tenure in the office, Dorothy Vaughan assigned her to a project in the Maneuver Loads Branch of the Flight Research Division, and Katherine's temporary position soon became permanent. She spent the next four years analyzing data from flight tests and worked on the investigation of a plane crash caused by **wake turbulence**. As she was wrapping up this work, her husband died of cancer in December 1956.

The 1957 launch of the Soviet satellite *Sputnik* changed history—and Katherine Johnson's life. In 1957, Katherine provided some of the math for the 1958 document Notes on Space Technology, a compendium of a series of 1958 lectures given by engineers in the Flight Research Division and the Pilotless Aircraft Research Division (PARD). Engineers from those groups formed the core of the Space Task Group, NACA's first official foray into space travel, and Katherine, who had worked with many of them since coming to Langley, "came along with the program" as the

....

wake turbulence the disturbance that forms behind an aircraft as it moves through the air

NACA became NASA later that year. She did **trajectory** analysis for Alan Shepard's May 1961 mission Freedom 7, America's first human spaceflight. In 1960, she and engineer Ted Skopinski coauthored Determination of Azimuth Angle at Burnout for Placing a Satellite Over a Selected Earth Position, a report laying out the equations describing an orbital spaceflight in which the landing position of the spacecraft is specified. It was the first time a woman in the Flight Research Division had received credit as an author of a research report.

In 1962, as NASA prepared for the orbital mission of John Glenn, Katherine Johnson was called upon to do the work that she would become most known for. The complexity of the orbital flight had required the

Rocket launches from Cape Canaveral on the Freedom 7 mission and first human spaceflight.

---

trajectory flight path an object follows through space

construction of a worldwide communications network, linking tracking stations around the world to IBM computers in Washington, D.C., Cape Canaveral, Florida, and Bermuda. The computers had been programmed with the orbital equations that would control the trajectory of the capsule in Glenn's Friendship 7 mission, from blast off to splashdown, but the astronauts were wary of putting their lives in the care of the electronic calculating machines, which were prone to hiccups and blackouts. As a part of the preflight checklist, Glenn asked engineers to "get the girl"—Katherine Johnson—to run the same numbers through the same equations that had been programmed into the computer, but by hand, on her desktop mechanical calculating machine. "If she says they're good," Katherine Johnson remembers the astronaut saying, "then I'm ready to go." Glenn's flight was a success and marked a turning point in the competition between the United States and the Soviet Union in space.

When asked to name her greatest contribution to space exploration, Katherine Johnson talks about the calculations that helped synch Project Apollo's Lunar Lander with the moon-orbiting Command and Service Module. She also worked on the space shuttle and the Earth Resources Satellite, and authored or coauthored

Katherine Johnson receives the Presidential Medal of Freedom from President Barack Obama on November 24, 2015.

twenty-six research reports. She retired in 1986, after thirty-three years at Langley. "I loved going to work every single day," she says. In 2015, at age 97, Katherine Johnson added another extraordinary achievement to her long list: President Obama awarded her the Presidential Medal of Freedom, America's highest civilian honor.

Mathematician Katherine Johnson at Work

by NASA.gov

Katherine Johnson began her career in 1953 at the National Advisory Committee for Aeronautics (NACA), the agency that preceded NASA, one of a number of African American women hired to work as "computers" in what was then their Guidance and Navigation Department, just as the NACA was beginning its work on space. Johnson became known for her training in geometry, her leadership, and her inquisitive nature. She was the only woman at the time to be pulled from the computing pool to work with engineers on other programs.

Johnson worked at Langley from 1953 until her retirement in 1986, making critical technical contributions that included calculating the trajectory of the 1961 flight of Alan Shepard, the first American in space. "The early trajectory was a **parabola**, and it was easy to predict

---

parabola a curve similar in shape to the path of a thrown object rising and then falling through the air

Katherine Johnson, pictured here in 1980, spent more than thirty years as a mathematician supporting the U.S. space program.

where it would be at any point," Johnson said. "Early on, when they said they wanted the capsule to come down at a certain place, they were trying to compute when it should start. I said, 'Let me do it. You tell me when you want it and where you want it to land, and I'll do it backwards and tell you when to take off.' That was my forte."

Johnson is also known for verifying the calculations made by electronic computers of John Glenn's 1962 launch to orbit and the 1969 Apollo 11 trajectory to the moon. She also worked on the space shuttle program and the Earth Resources Satellite and encouraged students to pursue careers in science and technology. She was awarded the Presidential Medal of Freedom, the nation's highest civilian honor, by President Barack Obama on Nov. 24, 2015.

Mary Jackson Biography

by Margot Lee Shetterly for NASA.gov

Date of Birth: April 9, 1921
Hometown: Hampton, Virginia
Education: B.S., Mathematics and Physical Science, Hampton Institute, 1942
Hired by NACA: April 1951
Retired from NASA: 1985
Date of Death: February 11, 2005
Actress Playing Role in *Hidden Figures:* Janelle Monáe

For Mary Winston Jackson, a love of science and a commitment to improving the lives of the people around her were one and the same. In the 1970s, she helped the youngsters in the science club at Hampton's King Street Community Center build their own wind tunnel and use it to conduct experiments. "We have to do something like this to get them interested in science," she said in an article for the local newspaper. "Sometimes they are not aware of the number of black scientists and don't even know of the career opportunities until it is too late."

Mary's own path to an engineering career at the NASA Langley Research Center was far from direct. A native of Hampton, Virginia, she graduated from Hampton Institute in 1942 with a dual degree in Math and Physical Sciences and accepted a job as a math teacher at a black school in Calvert County, Maryland. Hampton had become one of the nerve centers of the World War II home-front effort, and after a year of teaching, Mary returned home, finding a position as the receptionist at the King Street USO Club, which served the city's black population. It would take three more career changes—a post as a bookkeeper in Hampton Institute's Health Department, a stint at home following the birth of her son, Levi, and a job as an Army secretary at Fort Monroe—before Mary landed at the Langley Memorial Aeronautical Laboratory's segregated West Area Computing section in 1951, reporting to the group's supervisor Dorothy Vaughan.

After two years in the computing pool, Mary Jackson received an offer to work for engineer Kazimierz Czarnecki on the 4-foot by 4-foot Supersonic Pressure Tunnel, a 60,000 horsepower wind tunnel capable of blasting models with winds approaching twice the speed of sound. Czarnecki offered Mary hands-on experience conducting experiments in the facility, and eventually suggested that she enter a training program that would allow her to earn a promotion from mathematician to engineer. Trainees had to take graduate level math and physics in after-work courses managed by the University of Virginia. Because the classes were held at then-segregated Hampton High School, however, Mary needed special permission from the City of Hampton to join her white peers in the classroom. Never one to flinch in the face of a challenge, Mary completed the courses, earned the promotion, and in 1958 became NASA's first black female engineer. That same year, she co-authored her first report, "Effects of Nose Angle and Mach Number on Transition on Cones at Supersonic Speeds."

Mary Jackson began her engineering career in an era in which female engineers of any background were a rarity; in the 1950s, she very well may have been the only black female aeronautical engineer in the field. For nearly two decades she enjoyed a productive engineering career, authoring or co-authoring a dozen or so research reports, most focused on the behavior of the boundary layer of air around airplanes. As the years progressed, the promotions slowed, and she became frustrated at her inability to break into management-level grades. In 1979,

Staff of the Supersonic Pressure Tunnel pose for a photograph, taken in the 1950s. "Computers" in the front row include Mary Jackson at the far right.

seeing that the glass ceiling was the rule rather than the exception for the center's female professionals, she made a final, dramatic career change, leaving engineering and taking a demotion to fill the open position of Langley's Federal Women's Program Manager. There she worked hard to make an impact on the hiring and promotion of the next generation of NASA's female mathematicians, engineers, and scientists.

Mary Jackson at work at NASA Langley Research Center

Mary Jackson retired from Langley in 1985. Among her many honors were an Apollo Group Achievement Award and being named Langley's Volunteer of the Year in 1976. She served as the chair of one of the center's annual United Way campaigns, was a Girl Scout troop leader for more than three decades, and a member of the National Technical Association (the oldest African American technical organization in the United States). She and her husband Levi had an open-door policy for young Langley recruits trying to gain their footing in a new town and a new career. A 1976 Langley Researcher profile might have done the best job capturing Mary Jackson's spirit and character, calling her a "gentlelady, wife and mother, humanitarian, and scientist." For Mary Jackson, science and service went hand in hand.

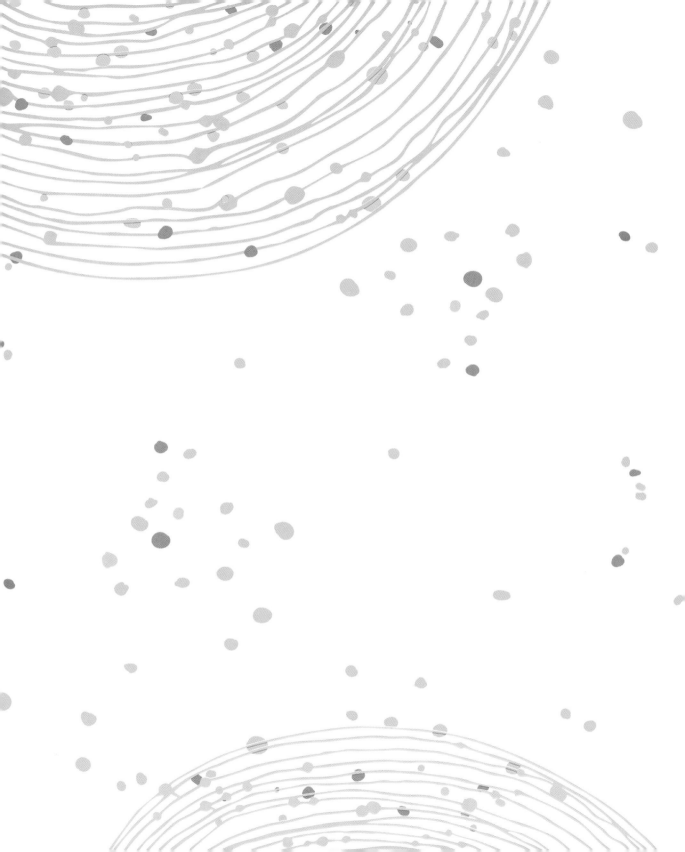

Dorothy Vaughan Biography

by Margot Lee Shetterly for NASA.gov

Date of Birth: September 20, 1910
Hometown: Kansas City, Missouri
Education: B.A., Mathematics,
Wilberforce University, 1929
Hired by NACA: December 1943
Retired from NASA: 1971
Date of Death: November 10, 2008
Actress Playing Role in *Hidden Figures:* Octavia Spencer

In an era when NASA is led by an African American man (Administrator Charles Bolden) and a woman (Deputy Administrator Dava Newman), and when recent NASA Center directors come from a variety of backgrounds, it's easy to overlook the people who paved the way for the agency's current robust and diverse workforce and leadership. Those who speak of NASA's pioneers rarely mention the name Dorothy

Vaughan, but as the head of the National Advisory Committee for Aeronautics (NACA) segregated West Area Computing Unit from 1949 until 1958, Vaughan was both a respected mathematician and NASA's first African American manager.

Dorothy Vaughan came to the Langley Memorial Aeronautical Laboratory in 1943, during the height of World War II, leaving her position as the math teacher at Robert Russa Moton High School in Farmville, Virginia, to take what she believed would be a temporary war job. Two years after President Roosevelt signed Executive Order 8802 into law, prohibiting racial, religious, and ethnic discrimination in the country's defense industry, the laboratory began hiring black women to meet the skyrocketing demand for processing aeronautical research data. Urgency and twenty-four hour shifts prevailed—as did Jim Crow laws, which required newly hired "colored" mathematicians to work separately from their white female counterparts. Dorothy Vaughan was assigned to the segregated West Area Computing unit, an all-black group of female mathematicians, who were originally required to use separate dining and bathroom facilities. Over time, both individually and as a group, the "West Computers" distinguished themselves with contributions to virtually every area of research at Langley.

The group's original section heads (first Margery Hannah, then Blanche Sponsler) were white. In 1949, Dorothy Vaughan was promoted to lead the group, making her the NACA's first black supervisor, and one of the NACA's few female supervisors. The Section Head title gave Dorothy rare laboratory-wide visibility, and she collaborated with other well-known (white) computers like Vera Huckel and Sara Bullock on projects such as compiling a handbook for algebraic methods for calculating machines. Vaughan was a steadfast advocate for the women of West Computing and even intervened on behalf of white computers in other groups who deserved promotions or pay raises. Engineers valued her recommendations as to the best "girls" for a particular project and for challenging assignments that they often requested she personally handle.

Dorothy Vaughan helmed West Computing for nearly a decade. In 1958, when the NACA made the transition to NASA, segregated facilities, including the West Computing office, were abolished. Dorothy Vaughan and many of the former West Computers joined the new Analysis and Computation Division (ACD), a racially and gender-integrated group on the frontier of electronic computing. Dorothy Vaughan became an expert FORTRAN programmer, and she also contributed to the Scout Launch Vehicle Program.

NASA's female human "computers," shown here in 1950, were hired to perform mathematical calculations. Dorothy Vaughan is seated at left.

Dorothy Vaughan retired from NASA in 1971. She sought, but never received, another management position at Langley. Her legacy lives on in the successful careers of notable West Computing alumni, including Mary Jackson, Katherine Johnson, Eunice Smith, and Kathryn Peddrew, and the achievements of second-generation mathematicians and engineers such as Dr. Christine Darden.

NASA Langley's Modern Figures Reflect on Changing Times and *Hidden Figures*

by Eric Gallard, NASA Langley Research Center, for NASA.gov

August 6, 2017

When an e-mail from the White House hit Debbie Martinez's inbox last year, she thought it was too good to be true.

"I thought it was spam," she said.

The message invited her and two NASA Langley Research Center employees for a screening of the movie *Hidden Figures*, which is based on the book of the same name that documented the lives and work of women like Katherine Johnson, Mary Jackson, and Dorothy Vaughan during the early days of the space race.

Martinez's friend and colleague Tahani Amer received the same and had the same reaction.

"I didn't even answer the e-mail for a couple of days," she said. Instead, she called Langley officials to confirm the legitimacy of the e-mail.

"I didn't believe it at first," she said.

After Amer learned the invitation was legit, she happily responded that she would attend.

"I remember when I first got the invite and Debbie called me on my cell," said Julie Williams-Byrd, a friend and colleague of Martinez and Amer. "She said, 'Julie? Is this for real? Don't play with me! It's on my bucket list to one day be invited to the White House!'"

NASA Langley engineer, Tahani Amer

Amer, Martinez and Williams-Byrd had just agreed to be "Modern Figures," representing Langley to highlight diversity and technical accomplishments since the days of the original Hidden Figures. There are Modern Figures at all NASA's field centers around the country.

"I think all three of us can tell you, we don't take it lightly," Williams-Byrd said. "We are prepared and we try to bring it wherever we go."

Amer echoed those thoughts: "You become a NASA image," she said.

NASA Langley engineer, Debbie Martinez

Supporting Each Other

Amer, Martinez, and Williams-Byrd, all engineers, have known each other for 25 years. When they started out, there weren't as many women at Langley as there are now.

"We kind of gravitated toward each other," Martinez said. "We're all in different fields so it's not like we ran into each other all the time."

"We're a very tight community here at Langley," Amer said. "We support each other a lot."

That support was galvanized when NASA reached out to Langley, seeking names to represent the agency as ambassadors in the lead-up to the *Hidden Figures* movie release.

"And somehow, headquarters decided the three of us would be the ones chosen," Williams-Byrd said.

"You can't really turn down these types of opportunities because if you're given this gift, you got to give it forward," Martinez said.

Amer said the unique backgrounds and accomplishments of each woman likely were factors in their selection. "Each of us brings something different to the table," she said.

Appreciating the Past

The trio believe they wouldn't have a seat at the table if not for the women who came before them. When asked to compare themselves to the women featured in *Hidden Figures*, Amer said there are some similarities.

"I see a lot struggles that we had to overcome to prove ourselves," she said.

Amer told of an experience she had presenting a paper at a conference in Nevada. She overheard people asking what she was doing there, questioning if she was out of her depth.

"It really hurt," said Amer.

Amer said she relies on her deep support system of family, friends, and colleagues. "Someone has to help you get over the hump," she said. "You have to have someone who always believes in you."

Progress and Pace

A lot of things have changed in the twenty-five years the three women have known each other—from the types of missions undertaken to the roles of women at Langley. They agree, though, that one thing has stayed constant— the need to help future generations advance.

Amer touts putting colleagues with potential in the spotlight to see what they can do.

"The most important thing is providing the opportunity," she said. "If you don't have the opportunity to do good work and get in the right project, you will never shine."

Martinez and Williams-Byrd have known what it is like to be honored by your peers, as they were past recipients of Women of Color in STEM awards.

"We do watch out for one another and we also watch out for those women who are coming up and helping them—giving them mentoring and information about what's available, what they can do and help them navigate the world," Williams-Byrd said.

One aspect they aim to continue with their newfound public roles is to help put a spotlight on deserving women by nominating young women to receive recognition and awards.

"There are different ways that we can help our more junior colleagues to shine and to be acknowledged," Williams-Byrd said. "When you're working really hard and doing good things, you want to be acknowledged."

Martinez said they also look out for more experienced women who are overlooked when it comes to recognition and awards.

"It's hard as a woman to really boast about yourself and take credit for the work that you've done because it's not in our nature," she said.

One example Amer gave was that she was invited to give a talk at Georgetown University in Washington, D.C., and met a young woman engineer who did not know her deputy center director at NASA's Goddard Space Flight Center in Greenbelt, Maryland. The young woman impressed Amer so much that she helped introduce her to Christyl Johnson, the deputy director for technology and research investments at Goddard.

"I feel, because of who I am and who we are, we need to help other women in the agency," she said.

Thinking About the Future

If you think the trio are superheroes for all they do for NASA, you're mistaken, Amer said. Their experiences and knowledge gleaned from an ever-changing atmosphere and the diverse workforce are what makes them who they are.

"We are together for a common cause, which is advancing NASA's missions," she said. "We bring our own experiences that make us stronger together."

The three say that as technology moves forward, so hopefully will opportunities for advancement and increased responsibility.

"I hope that NASA continues to keep its brand and continues to be a place of technical excellence," Williams-Byrd said. "We bring in the best and the

NASA Langley engineer,
Julie Williams-Byrd

brightest and those who are prepared to take on leadership roles."

New roles are something these women have become accustomed to handling during their time at Langley.

"All of us can say that we aren't doing what we were doing when we first came here," Williams-Byrd said. "We have changed tremendously."

The change is reflected when representing NASA, especially at events outside of Langley such as at schools. The *Hidden Figures* book and movie helped put STEM (science, technology, engineering, mathematics) on the map for young girls and women.

"I think that opens the door when they see us," Martinez said. "That just helps break these glass ceilings a little bit more for them."

Moments in History

A Ride in the Night

from Will Clark, Boy Adventurer *by Katharine E. Wilkie

It was 1779. Will Clark had grown into a tall boy of nine. Today he stood facing his father in the dining room of their Virginia home.

"He's too young," Ann Clark said quickly to her husband.

John Clark frowned. He was sitting in a big armchair with one foot on a stool in front of him. He looked hard at Will. "Yes, he's too young," John Clark agreed.

"But I can do it, Father," Will Clark said.

"Those horses must be delivered," Mr. Clark said slowly.

"But he's only a boy, John," his wife insisted.

Mr. Clark looked at Will. Few boys of his age were as tall and as broad-shouldered as this red-haired, blue-eyed lad. He could easily have been mistaken for eleven.

"This boy can do it," John Clark answered at last. "I know he can."

Will could hardly keep back a shout. He was really going to be trusted with this job.

"Listen carefully to me," said John Clark. "You must carry out my directions to the letter. Oh, if only I had not dropped that stone on my foot last week!"

"Don't worry, Father," said Will. "I'll do exactly as you say."

John Clark's voice dropped almost to a whisper. "You'll take the string of six horses to the ford at Plover's Creek. There you'll cross and follow the trail to Sugar Maple Hill. On the far side of the hill is a small tavern run by a man named Coleman. I've never seen him, so I can't describe him to you. But the password is 'Kentucky,' so don't give the horses to anyone who doesn't give it to you."

"Kentucky!"

"Hush!" commanded John Clark. "What better password is there for a man with a son on the Kentucky frontier?"

"And we'll go there someday," Will reminded him. "You promised, and so did George."

His father nodded. "Meanwhile, you must get those horses delivered. They'll be used in the Continental Army. General Washington needs them. He needs all the help every patriot can give. Take York with you. Sometimes two heads are better than one."

Will started out of the room on a run. His mother called him back. She looked at her youngest son for a long time. "Now I have six sons serving their country," she said softly.

Fifteen minutes later Will and York were riding away from home in the moonlight. Besides their own mounts, they had six horses to be delivered to Coleman's Inn.

Neither boy knew too well the part of the country to which he was going. But Will was certain he could find the place.

"You must be part bloodhound." York chuckled. "I'll bet you could find your way to Kentucky all by yourself."

"I'd like to try," Will answered. "But by the time I go, the route will be well marked."

"I won't mind if it is," said York. "You'll take me with you, won't you?"

"Of course. When the war is over, all of us are going. All my family and all yours. We'll make quite a procession, won't we? By that time my five brothers will be home from the army. I suppose they'll go, too. And of course there are Elizabeth, Lucy, Fanny, and Ann."

"I wish we were there now in a nice, warm house. It's cold out here tonight," said York with a shiver. His teeth chattered as he spoke. Somewhere in the distance a hoot owl gave a mournful sound. "Listen!"

"At least you know that's not an Indian on the warpath. All the Indians in Virginia are friendly ones," said Will. "Do you remember how the other boys and I used to imitate Indian calls and follow every traveler who came through the woods near home?"

"Yes, I do," York answered. "Look. Yonder is the ford."

In the distance Plover's Creek flowed peacefully in the moonlight. The boys had been riding for several hours. They were glad to come to this stage in their journey. The path to the ford lay clear and shining before them.

"Come on!" called Will. He kicked his horse's side slightly. "You follow behind, York, just to be certain everything is all right."

In a few minutes the boys rode up out of the water. The wet coats of the horses shone in the moonlight. The trail toward Sugar Maple Hill was clearly to be seen.

Will shivered slightly. "That water was chilly. I'll be glad to deliver these horses and warm myself before a good fire."

York sighed. "It seems as if I can taste Mama's bacon and hominy grits right now. I'm hungry."

"So am I," agreed his companion. "It can't be much longer now, York."

Nearly an hour later the boys looked down from a little rise into the valley below. They saw a large tavern. Smoke was curling from the chimney, even though the hour was early.

"There's our breakfast," York said hungrily. "What are we waiting for?"

"I don't know," Will said slowly. "There's something I don't like. I'm not certain what it is. Look, York." He pointed to a half dozen horses tied outside the tavern.

"Father said I should see a man. There's more than one man in the tavern."

"Well, after all, people do spend the night at taverns," York reminded him.

Will frowned. "Maybe I'm being extra careful, but I'm not going to take these horses down there yet. You lead them back into the woods and wait for me."

"All right," York grumbled. "But don't forget my stomach has just about grown to my backbone. I'm hungry!"

York turned with all the horses and led them into the surrounding woods. Will rode alone down to the tavern.

He dismounted outside the door. Then he tied his mare to the hitching rack with all the other horses. His heart was beating fast as he entered the building.

Once inside the main room he looked quickly about him. What he feared was true: a group of red-coated soldiers were sitting around a large pine table.

"Here's a new man for King George!" one of them called loudly.

Will swallowed hard as they turned to look at him. The British soldiers with their mugs and platters looked as big as giants. The landlord leaned over the counter. He had a long, sharp carving knife in his hand.

The boy tried to speak. For a moment his voice would not come. "I d-don't think the King could use me yet," he stammered.

Most of the men roared with laughter. They seemed to think the idea of Will being a soldier was very funny.

"He doesn't think the King could use him yet!" repeated one of the men. "He's right. King George doesn't want fighters as young as he is. Ha! Ha! Ha!"

Another soldier was watching Will closely. This man had not laughed so much as his companions. "What are you doing out so early, boy?" he demanded.

Will gave a start. He hoped the man did not notice it. He did some fast thinking. "I'm on the way to my aunt's house, sir."

"Where does she live?" asked the soldier. He kept his eyes fixed on Will.

"At Williamsburg."

"And you're going there alone?"

"There's no one to go with me. I'm an orphan. I spend half the time with my aunt, half the time with my grandmother down in the country," Will added.

He stole a glance at the other men. They were paying little attention to him. They were too busy talking and laughing and eating. Then the questioning soldier turned to them. "This boy may know something about the horses."

Will's heart was in his mouth. He had been right after all: there was something wrong here somewhere.

The man was still talking. "He may even have brought them with him."

"Nonsense, Brown!" insisted another man. "He's only a boy. No one would trust valuable horses to a boy!"

The soldier called Brown turned toward Will. His eyes were cold and dangerous. He twisted Will's shoulder crudely. "We're on the lookout for horses intended for the Continental Army. Do you know anything about them?"

"Ouch! You're hurting me!"

The man's roughness had brought real tears to Will's eyes. The boy was glad of it. The pain would excuse the look of fear on his face. But his great fear was for York, hidden back in the woods with the horses.

"Stop it, Brown," one of the men ordered. "I have a son at home about his age. You shan't mistreat this boy."

Brown scowled. "Even boys can be traitors. How do I know he isn't a lying little rebel?"

"Shut up, I tell you!" said the other soldier. "This lad knows nothing about any horses. Eat your breakfast, boy, and be on your way."

Will could hardly swallow the plate of ham and eggs that the innkeeper brought him. This man, too, gave him a keen look that did nothing to relieve his uneasiness.

Could he be the Mr. Coleman of whom his father had spoken? It didn't seem so from the way he scowled. He didn't look friendly at all.

As soon as Will had finished, he laid a coin on the table and stole out the door. Once astride his mare, he turned her head toward the woods.

"That's not the road to Williamsburg," a voice growled from the doorway.

The boy looked down to meet the scowling eyes of his enemy. "I was only getting my bearings. I know the road to Williamsburg."

He galloped off in the opposite direction of the one he wanted to take. York must wait with the horses. Will hoped with all his heart that the boy would remain hidden in the woods.

Once out of sight of the tavern, Will slid out of the saddle. He patted the mare's muzzle and led her off the road into the underbrush. "We won't have a trail to follow this time, girl," he told her. "But somehow we must get back to York and those horses."

The distance back was short, but the going was rough. The way was tangled with sharp briars and thick undergrowth. Several times Will became a little confused.

Finally, however, he came to the spot where York sat in a little clearing. Will drew a breath of relief when he saw him. The horses were standing quietly nearby.

"I thought you had deserted me," York moaned. "I thought I'd have to stay out here in these woods until I starved to death."

"That might be better than a rope around your neck," Will told him grimly. "That tavern is filled with British soldiers. I had trouble getting away from them."

York's eyes opened wide. "What shall we do now?" he asked.

"We must wait for them to leave," Will said. "We'll take turns watching. They'll have to be on their way before long."

The sun was high in the sky before the soldiers came out the tavern door. They mounted their horses and galloped away toward the north. The boys waited in the woods a while longer. At last they made their way slowly and cautiously down to the tavern.

The landlord's face lighted up with a smile as Will came in the door.

"So it's you again," he said. "You wouldn't be from Kentucky, would you?"

He said the word so loud and clearly that Will knew he had come to the end of his journey.

"No, I'm not from Kentucky," he answered. He too lingered on the word. "Neither are the horses hidden back in the woods, but maybe you'd like to have them anyway."

The landlord gave a hearty laugh. He laid a friendly hand on Will's shoulder. "That I would," he said. "I've been looking for them, and my son Edward will take them on their way tonight. My name is George Coleman."

Will gave a happy sigh. He had completed his mission successfully. He had finished the job. Now he could go home.

"I thought it was all over when you walked in on the King's men," said Mr. Coleman. "It wasn't safe for me to give you a signal of any kind. But you played your part well. You're a bright lad—a lad to help build America."

Will smiled as he and York rode away from the tavern toward home. He was proud because of Mr. Coleman's praise. But most of all he was proud because he had done something to help carry on the war.

Run, Kate Shelley, Run

by Julia Pferdehirt

Kate Shelley's home stood on a hill above Honey Creek and the railroad line that led to Moingona, Iowa. All her life Kate had heard the rush of water and the whistle of trains. All her life she had watched the Chicago and Northwestern Railway cars and heard the hissing black steam engines clack-clattering over Honey Creek Bridge.

Every train had a number and a whistle. When Kate's Pa was alive, he had taught her to recognize each train engine by the sound of its whistle. He'd been a section foreman for the Chicago and Northwestern until his death three years earlier in a railroad accident. After that, Kate and her mother fed the livestock, planted the garden, and sent the little ones off to school.

Kate was fifteen years old in July 1881, when the great storm began. It rained on Friday. By Saturday, market day, the ground was muddy, and still the rain poured down. On Sunday the roads were thick brown sponges,

sucking at boots and wagon wheels. The rain fell day and night. The following Wednesday, the sky paused to catch its breath. The day was oven-hot. Kate rushed to hang laundry to dry before the rain came again. Sure enough, by afternoon she saw more clouds, dark as midnight, rolling toward Honey Creek.

After nearly a week of rain, the creek was a wild bull, roaring and leaping, crashing against the high bluffs that caged it in on either side. Fence posts, rocks, and entire trees rolled and tumbled down the creek bed, colliding with the pilings of the bridge, causing it to creak and sway. Then the storm broke, and rain poured from the sky. The water rose.

The rising floodwaters began to seep into the barn, and Kate hurried down the hill to rescue the stock. She turned the animals out to higher ground and scrambled to save the baby pigs huddled on a haystack surrounded by water. Then Kate went up to the house and stared anxiously out the windows with her mother and nine-year-old sister, Mayme. The younger children were asleep.

It was nearly eleven o'clock when Kate heard Number 11's whistle. Long, short—long, short—screaming into the wind. The rumble of the engine grew louder as it crept along the line from Moingona to Boone, checking for washouts on the track. Suddenly Kate heard a crack like thunder, and another and another. With a sound like cannon fire, the Honey Creek trestle bridge, the engine, and four terrified crewmen crashed into the roaring water twenty feet below.

Kate pulled on her barn coat and a battered straw hat. "I'm going," she said.

Kate's mother gripped her arm. "No, Kate. You could be killed in that storm!"

Kate grabbed Pa's railroad lantern. "If Pa were out there, I'd go," she said. "I have to do it, Ma." With shaking hands, she lit the lantern and ran into the downpour and darkness to Honey Creek.

The water tossed trees and twisted metal like toys. Two men clung to branches surrounded by the wreckage; they were screaming for help. The two other crewmen had been washed away. Kate waved her lantern to say, "Hold on. Just hold on. I'll do something."

Before Kate could think of a way to help the men, a terrible thought struck her. The midnight express was scheduled to come in less than an hour. The train, its crew, and two hundred passengers were right now, right this minute, headed toward Honey Creek, not realizing that the bridge was out. It had sounded like cannon fire when Number 11 went down. It would sound like an entire war if the midnight express crashed into Honey Creek. Over two hundred people could die. She had to stop that train!

Kate gripped the lantern tighter and stumbled along the rails, following them like a road into the blackness and storm. She ran and fell, slipped and stumbled, toward the Moingona railroad station over a mile away.

Kate's chest burned. She was wet clear through and shaking with cold, but she could not stop. If it were Pa hanging on in Honey Creek or driving the midnight express, she would keep going. I must reach the station in time, she thought.

Between Honey Creek and the Moingona station, the railroad crossed the Des Moines River. The trestle bridge was high above the water and nearly seven hundred feet long. Kate dared not think of the railroad ties, a pace apart, only rain and sky between them and the river below.

The storm shook the Des Moines River bridge until it swayed and trembled. The rain fell even harder. Mud and water made the crossties slick and treacherous. How could anyone cross this bridge—caught between the wind, the rain, and the boiling, angry river?

Kate knelt down and crawled forward on her hands and knees. If it were Pa driving the midnight express toward Honey Creek, she would keep crawling. She could crawl for those two hundred people.

The wind blew her lantern out. She crept forward in the dark, feeling the railroad ties with her hands, using the cold metal rails as a guide.

Suddenly lightning flashed, and Kate saw a tree hurtling toward the bridge. Its tangled branches and massive trunk rolled and bounced in the current. It would hit the bridge! She remembered the crack of the pilings at Honey Creek and the cannon shot as the trestle collapsed. Kate clung to the crossties and prayed.

At the last second the current flipped the tree so the great trunk and its reaching limbs slipped between the pilings. Even then the branches tried to pull Kate from her perch above the river. She held on tighter and trembled.

"Only a little farther," Kate told herself when her hands finally felt mud and stones instead of empty air between the ties. She was safe across the bridge now; it was a half-mile to the station.

When she saw the station lights, Kate ran like a wild woman. Her wet skirt slapped and caught against her legs. Every breath hurt. She crashed into the station door and fell inside.

"Stop! Stop the train!" she gasped. "The engine— Honey Creek. Stop the train."

"The girl's crazy!" said one of the railroad men.

"Not on your life!" said the station agent. "That's Shelley's girl Kate."

Between gasps of air, Kate told them the Honey Creek Bridge had collapsed. "Two men are still alive," she said. "And the midnight express must be stopped."

The station agent telegraphed six miles west to Ogden to be sure the midnight express would not be allowed to continue in the storm. Then the railroad men and Kate borrowed a pusher engine and headed toward Honey Creek, blowing the whistle all the way, calling to the two stranded men to hold on a little longer.

At Honey Creek the bluffs had collapsed into the water. Kate led the rescuers to another bridge where they could cross and finally reach the engineer and brakeman. The two men were half-dead with exhaustion.

After that, Kate did not remember the engine puffing away toward the station. She did not remember her mother leading her to bed or piling blankets over her shaking body. She did not remember the gray-and-rose sky of dawn.

The same telegraph that had warned Ogden Station to hold the midnight express sent news of Kate's bravery from city to city. Within days, newspapers all over the nation were calling her the "Iowa heroine."

While Kate lay in bed recovering from that terrible night, every train passing the farmhouse blew its whistle in her honor. Then the people of Iowa awarded her a gold medal, and the railroad gave her one hundred dollars and a lifetime railroad pass.

The nation honored Kate, too. However, the honor most dear to her came from the railroad men themselves. As long as she lived in Moingona, Iowa, they recognized brave Kate in their own special way. Whenever she wanted to ride the Chicago and Northwestern, they stopped the train just for her. A station stop was not good enough. They stopped the train right in front of the little farmhouse on Honey Creek.

In 1900 a new bridge was built across the Des Moines River and named for Kate Shelley. And after her death, the Order of Railway Conductors and Brakemen placed a memorial to their Iowa heroine. "Hers is a deed bound for legend … a story to be told until the last order fades and the last rail rusts."

Young Frederick Douglass
The Slave Who Learned to Read

by Linda Walvoord Girard

In 1826 eight-year-old Frederick Bailey arrived in Baltimore. He had been sent from a plantation in the country to be the slave of Hugh Auld, his wife Sophia (or "Miz Sopha," as Frederick called her), and their young son Tommy.

For the first time in his life, Frederick had a straw bed and enough to eat. He wore trousers instead of a tattered, knee-length shirt, and instead of scooping his meals from a trough, he sat at a dinner table. And his mistress was very kind.

After dinner Mrs. Auld would often get her Bible and read aloud. One night, when Mr. Auld was gone, she read from the Book of Job. Suddenly, Frederick understood that the marks on a page could tell a story. He gathered his courage and asked Miz Sopha to teach him to read. Since she was getting ready to teach Tommy the ABCs anyway, Mrs. Auld agreed that Frederick could listen.

One day Mr. Auld came home while Mrs. Auld was teaching the boys. Miz Sopha bragged that Frederick was learning to read, and wasn't it amazing? Wasn't it amusing?

Mr. Auld sent Frederick out of the room. Then he began to lecture his wife. Teaching a slave was against the law, he told her. A slave who could read would be "spoiled." He would get ideas. He'd want to write as well, and if he could write, there was no telling what mischief he'd dream up. From his listening place outside the door, Frederick heard Mrs. Auld promise never to teach him again.

Now that he knew reading was forbidden, Frederick was determined to learn. If a newspaper was blowing about in the street, Frederick picked it up. If somebody left a schoolbook on the playground, it went home with him. And on errands, he studied street names and the packages and signs in stores. He spelled things out, and his reading got smoother and faster.

White schoolboys who had become his friends told him to get a book of great speeches called the *Columbian Orator*. In that book, they said, a slave debates his master and wins his freedom!

Frederick blacked boots to get the fifty cents he needed. He walked to a bookstore and bought the *Columbian Orator*. In it he discovered eloquent speeches from history, including the dialogue between master and slave. He read the speeches over and over until he understood them all. But could a slave truly win freedom by argument? he wondered. Would whites listen if a slave spoke? As his master, Mr. Auld, had feared, this slave had gotten ideas.

Frederick often played and did chores in the shipyards of Baltimore. He watched as the carpenters sawed and shaped pieces of lumber. On each piece, they wrote the initials for a part of the ship.

"What's that, Massa?" Frederick would ask.

"That's the letter *S*."

"Oh, the letter *S*. And what does that mean?"

"Means 'starboard.'"

"*S*, starboard. Yes, Massa, I'll remember that," he'd say. "And what's that, Massa?"

"The letter *L* – '**larboard**.'"

"Why, I'll remember that, Massa." And so on.

---

larboard means the same as *port*, the left side of a ship (*starboard* refers to the right side)

When the carpenters went to eat, Frederick would copy the letters. He knew if he could learn a few letters, he could learn the rest as well.

Often, when Frederick met white boys, he would suggest a writing contest. Using chalk, he'd draw the letters he knew on the pavement or on a wall. "Beat that if you can," he'd say.

The other boys would scrawl letters he didn't know, laughing at the idea that a slave boy could win a writing contest. Frederick lost the contests. But he would copy the new letters.

In the evening, in his small room above the kitchen, Frederick struggled on. He copied the tiny letters from a hymn book and a Bible he'd found in the house. He "borrowed" Tommy's old copybooks—small booklets in which students practiced penmanship. Frederick made his own practice letters in the empty spaces under Tommy's writing. He could have been whipped for messing up Tommy's precious keepsake schoolbooks, but luckily he was not found out. He slipped the books back into their places, and no one ever noticed the extra writing. By the time he was thirteen, Frederick could read and write very well.

A year later Frederick was given to a new master— Hugh Auld's brother, Thomas, who lived in the village of St. Michael's, Maryland.

When other slaves in St. Michael's learned that Frederick could read, they asked him to teach a Sunday school. The class met secretly in a free black man's house where there were desks, spelling books, and Bibles. During the second week, Thomas Auld burst in with a white mob. The men broke up the school with clubs and warned the students never to meet again.

Thomas Auld sent Frederick to a cruel slave "breaker" named Edward Covey. Frederick worked in Covey's fields from dawn to dark. Covey often whipped him for no reason. Soon Frederick's back was covered with scars, and he nearly lost an eye from a beating.

One hot summer morning, Covey started to beat him again. Frederick fought back. "I won't let you beat me," he said over and over. Their struggle lasted two hours. To Frederick's amazement, Covey finally gave up and never tried to beat him again.

When Frederick's year with Covey came to an end, Thomas Auld hired him out to a farmer named William Freeland. Then he lent him back to his brother Hugh in Baltimore.

Starving for educated companionship, Frederick joined a club of free young black people called the East Baltimore Mental Improvement Society. Tall and poised, the handsome Frederick Bailey stood out in the group.

It was here that he met a special, gentle young woman named Anna Murray.

Meanwhile, Hugh Auld decided to "rent" Frederick in the shipyards. Each Friday Frederick had to hand his master his wages—at first $6.50 a week, later $9.00. That was more than some of the white dockworkers earned, and once, jealous workers severely beat him. His life had become impossible. And as long as he was a slave, he could never marry Anna. Slaves could not sign papers or make legal ties such as marriage.

When he was twenty, Frederick decided to make a daring escape. With money Anna lent him, he would buy a ticket and go north by train.

Frederick knew that a black person traveling north would have to show papers proving he or she was free. And "free papers" were legal documents with official seals. Frederick couldn't fake these.

A good friend, a free black sailor named Benny, lent Frederick his sailor's "protection paper." This showed that Benny was registered as a seaman with an American shipping company. Across the top of this certificate, a big American eagle spread its wings. Below was a description of Benny.

It was a risky plan. If Frederick were caught, he would be sold south into harsh slavery. And Benny could go to jail.

Frederick made his run for freedom on September 3, 1838. He promised to write Anna as soon as he was safe. Because she was free, she could come north to meet him.

Frederick carefully planned every detail. He wore a sailor's red shirt, tarpaulin hat, and black neckerchief, loosely tied. He knew it could be dangerous for a black man to wait in the station with luggage, so he hired a cabdriver to race the train with his bag and toss it to him at the very last moment.

With Benny's paper, he settled into the "Negro car." His heart was pounding, but he acted calm.

The conductor came through and checked the papers of several free black passengers. "I suppose you have your free papers?" he asked Frederick.

"I never carry my free papers to sea with me," said Frederick. "I have a paper with the American eagle on it that will carry me around the world." With this he pulled out the impressive-looking sailor's protection paper. The conductor never checked to see if Frederick matched the description of the paper's owner.

Frederick's luck held, and the day after his escape, he arrived in New York City. His money was nearly gone, and he had to sleep on the docks one night. But friendly sailors warned him that the docks were patrolled for runaways, and the next night a sailor named Stewart took him to find David Ruggles, a free black abolitionist in New York.

While staying with Ruggles, Frederick wrote to Anna. She hurried north, and they were married on the 15th of September.

For safety, Frederick changed his name from Bailey to Douglass, and shortly afterward he got a job in a shipyard in New Bedford, Massachusetts. In his spare time, he began speaking about his life as a slave and the evil of a system that bought and sold human beings. He toured New England states as a speaker for the Massachusetts Anti-Slavery Society. Eloquent and passionate, Douglass held his audiences spellbound.

Because of his eloquence, many people did not believe that Douglass had ever been illiterate and a slave. To convince the doubters, in 1845 he published an autobiography, the *Narrative of the Life of Frederick Douglass*. In it he revealed his slave name and the name and location of his master. Now he was in greater danger of being seized and returned to slavery. He left for England, where he stayed for two years giving lectures for the abolitionist cause. In 1846 English friends bought his freedom from Thomas and Hugh Auld for about $700.

A year later Frederick and Anna moved to Rochester, New York, where Douglass established the *North Star*, an antislavery newspaper. Their home became a station on the Underground Railroad.

Douglass continued to work for the rights of black people. He fought for job equality and for integration in schools and churches and on trains. When traveling, he would sit in one of the railroad cars reserved for white passengers. Sometimes angry railroad workers dragged him out of his seat.

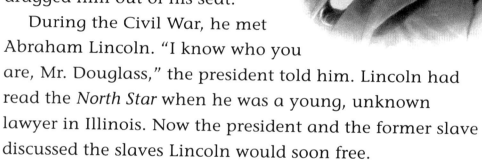

During the Civil War, he met Abraham Lincoln. "I know who you are, Mr. Douglass," the president told him. Lincoln had read the *North Star* when he was a young, unknown lawyer in Illinois. Now the president and the former slave discussed the slaves Lincoln would soon free.

Douglass went on to become Recorder of Deeds in the District of Columbia and later served as U.S. minister to Haiti. He also wrote two more autobiographies.

By the time of his death, Frederick Douglass, the slave who'd taught himself to read and write, had become the most important black leader of his time. Writer, orator, publisher, reformer, and statesman, he died in 1895 at the age of seventy-eight.

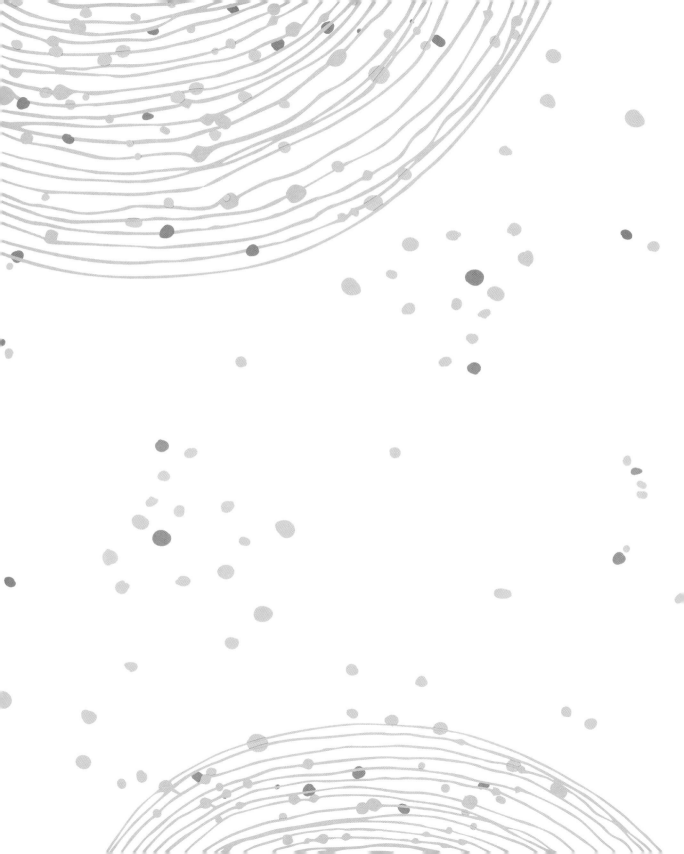

The Most Famous Woman in America

from Clara Barton: Founder of the American Red Cross
by Augusta Stevenson

One night in 1867 a large hall in Washington, D.C., was crowded with people. The greatest of American war nurses was to speak—Miss Clara Barton.

She had nursed sick and wounded soldiers in the Civil War of 1861–1865. She had been right up at the front, too! She was always in danger. Sometimes she was under enemy fire.

Miss Barton was now the most famous woman in America. She had done the greatest things for wounded soldiers that had ever been done by anyone in the United States.

She had found a way to save lives.

She hadn't liked the way the army took care of the wounded. She said their hospitals were splendid but too far from the battlefields. Many men died on the way, before they received treatment. Miss Barton said they should be treated at the front, as soon as they could be carried off the field.

Her plan had been adopted. Aid stations were now set up near every battlefield. Thousands of soldiers had been saved by them.

Their families were grateful to Miss Barton. The whole nation was grateful. People loved the sound of her name.

Tonight a group of young nurses was in a box to the left of the stage.

"Just imagine!" exclaimed one. "Clara Barton was the first woman nurse to go the battlefield—the very first in America."

"She had a hard time getting permission," said another. "General after general refused. They said it was no place for a woman."

"But that didn't stop Clara," said the third, smiling. "She went to other generals, army doctors, chaplains, quartermasters, colonels, and captains.

"She went to everyone she knew and everyone her friends knew. Finally she succeeded. She obtained permission to join the Army of the Potomac in 1862."

"Hurahh!" cried one, and all the white caps nodded.

"How could she do that?" asked a new nurse. "I thought she was timid."

The nurse from Massachusetts answered. "She was. She still is. Her relatives say that she dreads these lectures."

"Why is she speaking, then?"

"To get more help for sick and wounded soldiers. She is devoting all her time and energy to this. She has spoken in all the large cities in the East, and she is still lecturing to large crowds."

The new nurse shook her head. "How can she be a good speaker if she is so bashful?"

"Her relatives say she forgets herself when she begins to talk about the needs of soldiers. She becomes another person, with the courage to face any audience anywhere. Just wait. You'll see what I mean. You'll love her."

"I love her anyway," said the new nurse. "I think she is wonderful."

Again white caps nodded in agreement. They all thought Clara Barton was wonderful.

In the next box was a group of young soldiers. All carried canes or crutches.

"I am glad I'll get to see Nurse Barton again," said one. "She saved my life in the battle of Cedar Mountain."

"She saved me, too," said another. "I had been wounded for a long time. The orderlies wouldn't have found me if It hadn't been for her lanterns. She brought them in her supply wagon."

"They wouldn't have found a good many of us," said the third. "There weren't any candles or any lanterns in our camp. Our supply wagon hadn't come up."

"I don't see how Nurse Barton could get her wagon up to the front with her supplies," said a fourth.

"There's a lot of difference between a single four-mule wagon and a train of 'em, four or five miles long."

"That's true, Lucien. Anyway, an angel from heaven couldn't have been more welcome. We were starving, and she brought food."

"Do you remember the corn husks our doctors were using for bandages?" asked Will. "And do you remember the rolls of soft white bandages that Miss Barton brought?"

The others nodded and smiled.

"She was a real manager," said Joe. "In about three minutes she had things moving."

"She had fires made, kettle swung, water boiling, and food unpacked in no time at all," said another soldier.

"And she herself was making gruel," said Lucien. "Talk about angels from heaven!"

"In more ways than you can count," added James. "She wanted to live the way we boys lived. She didn't want comforts we couldn't have."

"That's a fact," agreed Joe. "I know she refused a carpet someone offered for her tent. She said soldiers were sleeping on the ground."

"She wouldn't take anything but a soldier's pay," said Robert. "She told me that herself."

"If she said it, it's true," declared Lucien.

The others nodded gravely.

Across the hall in a box to the right, there were four army doctors and surgeons who knew her well. All of them had worked with Nurse Barton at the front.

"She was the bravest woman I ever saw," said one.

"She helped me at the battle of Antietam," said another. "We were so close to the front that our faces were black with the smoke of powder."

"She waded in the mud at Falmouth," said the third. "She was helping the orderlies look for wounded men."

"Clara Baron never ran away from anything she thought was her duty," declared the fourth.

"No! Never!" agreed the others.

In an adjoining box were four army officers. Miss Barton had worked in their camps. All of them knew her well.

"I have often thought of her narrow escapes," said a general. "She was often under enemy fire. Once her skirt was riddled with bullets when she was crossing a bridge that was being shelled. She never seemed to be afraid."

"And such a bridge!" exclaimed a major. "It was just small boats close together and rocking with the strong current. It's a wonder she didn't fall into the river."

The captain smiled. "She told me afterward she had practiced for this when she was a girl. She learned to cross a river on teetering logs."

"It was a good thing she learned to ride horseback when she was young," said a colonel. "One day we had to ride at breakneck speed to escape from the enemy. She kept up with us."

"It looks as if she had been getting ready for this war all her life," said the general. "She was an athlete from the time she was thirteen."

"That's the reason she was able to stand the hardships of war," said the colonel. "A weaker woman wouldn't have lasted one day."

Now all talking stopped, for the meeting began. The Reverend William Fisher came on the stage.

He had charge of the meeting. He was followed by a lady. She was small, and she had dark eyes and hair. Her face was pleasant and kind.

The instant she appeared there was a thunder of applause. The large audience rose to its feet and a thousand voices called, "Miss Barton! Miss Barton!" The little lady bowed, smiled, and waved her hand. The applause went on and on. Miss Barton waved again and again.

At last the people were quiet and she began to speak. She told something about her work as a nurse in the army camps. But she talked more about the needs of soldiers who were still in hospitals.

When she finished there was long applause.

Then again the audience rose and stood until she had left the stage.

They couldn't do enough to show how much they loved and respected her.

President of American Red Cross

Fifteen years later, in 1882, another great crowd of people was in this same hall in Washington, D.C., to hear Miss Clara Barton speak.

Again she was the most famous woman in the United States. Again she had started something that had never been done before by anyone, man or woman, in this country.

She had founded the Red Cross in America.

Everyone in the crowded hall was talking about this. They all knew that Miss Barton had worked for years to get this country to join the International Red Cross. It had been established in Europe twenty years before. But America had been slow to join. Many officials didn't see the need for a Red Cross chapter here.

Clara Barton in 1881, the year she founded the Red Cross in the United States

"We won't have another war in this country," they said. "It is impossible."

Miss Barton didn't agree with them. She remembered the Civil War too well.

"There will be other wars," she said, "and we must be ready to take better care of the soldiers who are wounded."

She went to the White House to talk with President Hayes about the Red Cross.

Later on she went to see President Garfield. Still later she talked with President Arthur.

She talked with senators and representatives. She made public speeches in all parts of the country.

At last, under President Arthur, the United States signed the treaty with sixteen other countries. Now our country was a member of the International Red Cross.

This new chapter, The American Red Cross, had made Miss Barton its first president. The meeting tonight was in her honor.

Now the officers of the Red Cross were coming onto the stage and people began to applaud the woman who was responsible for this treaty.

There was no need to tell the audience which person on the stage was Miss Barton. They had seen her picture many times in the newspapers recently. Her hair was gray now, but her dark eyes were as bright as ever. She was still small and slender.

There was a thunder of applause when the people saw her. Everyone stood, and hundreds of voices cheered her.

The gray-haired lady bowed and smiled and waved her hand. Again and again she tried to speak, but the applause went on and on.

At last there was quiet and she began to speak to them. Everyone listened intently.

She said this Red Cross treaty among nations was a great and noble deed. Her heart was singing with happiness because her own country had now put its seal on the treaty. She told them that the Red Cross could serve in time of peace as well as during a war.

There were only a few Red Cross rules, she explained. The most important was that all men who were wounded in war would be cared for. It did not matter whether they were friends or enemies, black, white, yellow, or red.

The next most important rule was that no Red Cross workers, doctors, or nurses would be captured or put in prison by the enemy.

"The American chapter has now added one more rule for the United States," Miss Barton said. "It will help whenever there is a fire, flood, cyclone, hurricane, earthquake, or other disaster where it can be of use.

"It will go also wherever there is an epidemic such as yellow fever, typhus, or smallpox, either in this country or in another country.

"It will be ready to serve whenever it can relieve human suffering. The homeless and the sick will be given shelter, medicine, food, and clothing regardless of their ability to pay.

"All of this aid will be free. Not one sufferer will be asked to pay a penny.

"The money for all this will be given by those who are able to help. The fortunate will aid the unfortunate.

"When there is peace we will train volunteer workers who can care for the wounded in time of war. We will prepare medical supplies to be ready when they are needed. Will you help us?"

"Yes! Yes!" shouted many people.

"We will have trained people ready to go immediately to a place where there is a flood, a fire, a tornado, or any other disaster. We will provide food and temporary shelter for all those unfortunate men, women, and children who are left homeless and hungry. We will have supplies ready to help those who are hurt or sick. We will give immediate help when there is an epidemic. Will you help us?"

"Yes! Yes!" shouted the people.

"I myself am serving without pay and so are these officers. Our only thought is to make the American Red Cross a success. Will you help us?"

"Yes! Yes!" cried the great audience. Then they stood again and applauded until Miss Barton left the stage.

"There has never been anyone like her in the world," said an old man.

"Never! Never!" said all who heard.

Opinion and Persuasion

Make Your Own Microscope

Last week, my little sister knocked my microscope off the kitchen table. It broke, of course, so I went to the mall to buy a new one. But when I stopped into a store called Science Adventure, I was stunned by what I found. The microscope my sister broke costs $144.99! I'm 11 years old. I don't have that kind of money. No one my age does. Luckily, I found out that I didn't need that much money. I realized I didn't have to buy a new microscope. I discovered that I could instead turn my smartphone into a microscope. So that's just what I did. It turns out that it was a great way to save cash, to learn a lot, and to create an effective tool for scientific exploration.

The best thing about making a smartphone microscope is that it costs almost nothing. The only supplies I needed were a laser pointer, a bit of **poster tack**, a flashlight, some white paper, and clear plastic (Emerson). Honestly, I had most of that stuff at home already. I bought the rest of it right there at the mall, and I paid a grand total of $7.99 for everything. That's right:

poster tack a putty-like, reusable, pressure-sensitive adhesive

$7.99. Now, my weekly allowance is $5. That means it took me less than two weeks' worth of allowance money to buy the materials for my project. In comparison, a replacement microscope at Science Adventure would have cost me 29 weeks' worth of allowance money. Right off the bat, I'd saved myself $137. It was a great start.

Another excellent thing about this project was how much it taught me. As I read articles, followed directions, and watched online videos about what to do, I learned quite a bit. For example, I learned that lasers were first created as "an outgrowth of a suggestion made by Albert Einstein" more than 100 years ago (Hecht). I also learned that all laser pointers generate light with **laser diodes**. That light then passes through small lenses to focus it ("Laser Pointers Information"). I never knew any of that stuff before. Once I got to work, I also learned how easy it was to remove those lenses. And, of course, I learned how to attach one of those lenses to a smartphone so it can act like a magnifying glass.

a laser pointer

laser a device that uses vibration of atoms or molecules to create a narrow light beam that has a small frequency range

diodes electronic devices with two electrodes (used to make electrical contact with a nonmetallic part of an electrical circuit), used for changing alternating current into direct current

Finally, this whole process left me with a terrific tool. In some ways, my new smartphone microscope is just as good as my old microscope. In other ways, it's even better. For example, just like with my old microscope, I can enlarge whatever I am observing to an image up to 175 times its actual size. That is more than powerful enough to view the crystal structure of salt or the brickwork pattern of skin cells. But there's also the fact that my smartphone microscope is light. It's portable. I can take it with me anywhere. Plus, using its video function, I can even record whatever I'm looking at. That means I can capture motion and changes over time. Next week, I'm going to look at some pond water and record the movement of the bacteria in it. I couldn't do anything like that with my old, heavy microscope!

Now, I know what some people might say. They'll argue that not everyone has a smartphone. They'll say that the low cost of making a microscope like mine doesn't factor in the price of the phone itself. They might even say that they don't have the skill to build their own smartphone microscope. In response, let me say two things. One,

A smartphone microscope shows butterfly wing detail.

I never said the solution to my problem would work for everyone. I'm only saying that it's a good idea for people who already have smartphones. It's a bit like buying a special **app** that lets you do even more with your phone! Two, it is easy to build this type of microscope. Believe me, I'm not a mechanical whiz. I can barely pump up the tires on my bike. So if I can do this, anyone can do it.

Since I built my smartphone microscope, I've been very satisfied. I was able to keep the money I would have spent in my bank account, where it is earning **interest** every day. I found out lots of interesting facts and information about lasers and how lenses work. And, most important, I created a microscope that works great and has allowed me to continue to learn about the world around me. I call that a major success.

Works Cited

Emerson, Sarah. "How to Turn Your Smartphone Into a Microscope." *Motherboard*, 1 Apr. 2016, motherboard.vice.com/en_us/article/8q8q7v/how-to-turn-your-smartphone-into-a-microscope.

Hecht, Jeff. "Laser." *Encyclopædia Britannica*, Encyclopædia Britannica, Inc., 2017.

"Laser Pointers Information." *Engineering360*, www.globalspec.com/learnmore/optical_components_optics/lasers/laser_pointers.

....

app *application*, particularly in the sense of, for example, apps for mobile devices such as smartphones

interest money earned by a savings account; that is, money paid by a bank on money deposited and left in a savings account at the bank

Stick to Real Microscopes

All scientists seek information. Naturally, they want that information to be precise. They want it to be accurate. So they use tools to get it. Some tools are simple: beakers, test tubes, and timers. Other tools are complex:

microscopes, computers, and electronic scales. The simple tools used by scientists are fairly cheap. The complex tools are not. So I was not shocked when I read a piece about the high cost of microscopes.

I was surprised, however, when the author suggested that people should not pay for pricey microscopes. Rather, she said, people should turn their smartphones into microscopes. She argued that doing so was cheap. She insisted that converted phones work as well as or better than real microscopes (Emerson).

Let me just say, right now, that I wish that she was correct. It would be terrific if she was right. Unfortunately, I do not think she is. In fact, I think she is wrong on both counts. Turning a smartphone into a microscope is not cheap, and it does not create a great scientific tool. In my opinion, people should not do it.

The author of the piece I read began by focusing on costs. She stated that a decent microscope costs between $150 and $300. On this point, we agree. She then claimed that the items needed for a smartphone conversion cost about $10 (Emerson). At first glance, this looked like a major point in favor of the smartphone microscope. I admit that I was intrigued. Creating a microscope for just $10 sounded great to me.

Then I took a closer look at her numbers. I found, unfortunately, that they are way off. Ten dollars is not the real cost of conversion. Why? Because $10 does not include the cost of one pretty important item. In fact, I would argue that the missing item is the most important one. It is the smartphone itself.

The cheapest smartphone costs about $100. Right away, that puts the cost of conversion at $110. But cheap phones come with serious security risks. Accounts can get hacked. Personal information can be stolen. To avoid such risks, it is necessary to have a decent, safe smartphone.

Those don't cost $100. They cost between $250 and $400 (Dunn). So an accurate estimate of the cost of creating a smartphone microscope—one that includes the price of the phone itself—is more like $260 to $410. That's a lot more than ten bucks.

Indeed, that's equal to or more than the cost of a good real microscope. So there are no savings to be had here. Stating that one can make a smartphone microscope for a few dollars is flat-out false. It is like stating that one can get a red sports car for the price of a can of paint. There is also the small matter of paying for the sports car itself. Anyway, I think it is clear that smartphone microscopes are not cheaper than real microscopes.

But what about the author's second position? What about her claim that smartphone microscopes are just as good as or better than real microscopes? Well, a closer look reveals some problems there, as well.

The most powerful smartphone microscopes can magnify objects up to 350 times their actual size. That sounds impressive. But it pales in comparison to what a real microscope can do. A mid-level real microscope can magnify objects up to 2000 times their actual size. Let those numbers sink it. They say that a real microscope is five to six times more powerful than a smartphone microscope.

And what does that mean in the lab? Well, imagine

looking at a sample of blood. With a real microscope, one would see individual red blood cells, their specific shapes, and their distinct movements. A smartphone microscope would give the observer a very different picture. Suddenly, the sample would look like just a hazy collection of tiny red blobs (Manea). Remember, scientists seek to gather precise and accurate information. But the information gathered with the smartphone microscope would be less precise and less accurate. It would be less useful. Again, when the two are compared, the smartphone microscope comes up short.

The piece I read also insisted that smartphone microscopes are better because they let users take video of what they observe. That is certainly good and useful. Being able to take video is valuable. And I do not intend to argue against that value. Rather, I will just say that one does not need a smartphone microscope to take video. I found several real microscopes that come with digital cameras and video recorders. They can record videos just as easily as a smartphone microscope, but they can do so at much higher magnification. Several cost around $300 (Gates). Again, the real microscope is the better scientific tool.

Now, I am reasonable. I accept that there are some good things about smartphone microscopes. For instance, they are portable. They can be easily brought out into the field. That is an important thing, for sure. But its importance should not be overstated. Just because something is easily transported does not erase its other **shortcomings**. A spoon is more portable than a large shovel, but I would not want to dig a trench with a spoon.

Turning a smartphone into a microscope may be easy. It may make it simpler to observe certain things outside the lab. But once all of the costs are included, it is just as expensive as a real microscope. Further, it has only a fraction of the power of a real microscope. And it does not offer any features that a decent real microscope does not. In short, a smartphone microscope is a **novelty**. It is not a suitable replacement for a real microscope.

Works Cited

Dunn, Jeff. "The 9 best affordable smartphones you can buy." *Business Insider,* Business Insider, 9 Apr. 2017, www.businessinsider.com/best-cheap-phones-buying-guide-oneplus-moto-g-2017-4/#the-best-100-phone-with-major-caveats-blur1-hd-1.

Emerson, Sarah. "How to Turn Your Smartphone Into a Microscope." *Motherboard*, 1 Apr. 2016, motherboard.vice.com/en_us/article/8q8q7v/how-to-turn-your-smartphone-into-a-microscope.

Gates, Steve. "20 Best USB & Digital Microscope Reviews (Oct. 2017)." IND Reviews, 2 Oct. 2017, indreviews.com/best-microscope/.

Manea, Aurel. *Blood on 1000x Microscope HD 1080p*, YouTube, 31 Dec. 2011, www.youtube.com/watch?v=9va0KPrVExs.

shortcomings flaws; failings

novelty something new or unusual, but not very useful

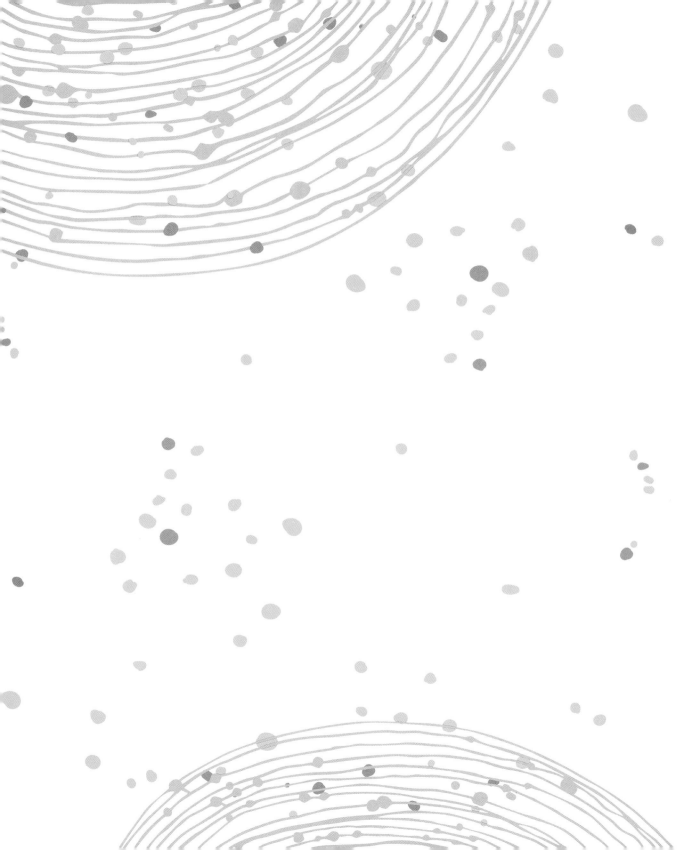

Solar Power for Public Buildings

olar power is electrical energy drawn from the sun. Solar power is clean; it is good for the earth. Solar power is renewable; the world will never run out of it. And solar power is plentiful; the sun provides the earth with more energy in one hour than the entire planet uses in one year (Morton 19). Yet, today, solar power creates only about 1 percent of the world's electricity (Schmalensee xi).

Why is creating electricity with solar power so uncommon? Is it because people have not figured out how to use the sun's energy effectively? No. Is it because other energy sources are cleaner or more abundant? Certainly not. Is it because creating electricity from solar power is too expensive? Again, no.

There is, in fact, no good reason that solar energy is not more widely used. Its underuse is foolish. It is illogical. It is unacceptable. It must change. America must increase its use of solar power, and California must lead the way.

Solar power for public buildings
will be good for California.

Thirty-nine million people live in California ("Quick Facts"). By population, it is the nation's largest state. California has hundreds of towns and cities. In those towns and cities are thousands of public buildings. And each one requires electricity. California should power all public buildings with solar energy.

Why? Using solar power in this way will be good for the state's economy. It will be good for its environment. It will be good for its people.

Powering public buildings with solar energy will create jobs. That is obvious. Workers will have to build solar panels. Truck drivers will have to deliver them. Some technicians will have to install them. Others will have to maintain them. All of these people will earn good wages. And as they spend those wages, they'll support other businesses. That will create a positive economic ripple effect ("Benefits of Renewable Energy Use").

But that is not all. The shift to solar will also lower the state's overall energy bill. Tax money once spent on energy costs will fund other projects. Roads will be updated. Bridges will be rebuilt. New train lines will be laid out. New parks will be born. Again, these projects will all create jobs. Again, the state's economy will grow.

Using solar power in public buildings will also help the environment. Solar panels do not give off harmful gases. They do not produce toxic chemicals. So pollution levels will drop ("Benefits of Renewable Energy Use"). Big cities will have less smog. There will be fewer health problems from breathing dirty air. Rivers and streams will also be less contaminated. Drinking water will be cleaner. Wildlife will flourish.

Further, the state will reduce its use of fossil fuels (Walsh). Fossil fuels include oil, coal, and natural gas. These natural resources are limited. Once they disappear, they will not return. So using less of them is always good.

Powering public buildings with solar energy will make people's lives better, too. Power blackouts will be

More solar power means less pollution. Here, downtown Los Angeles is covered in a haze of smog in March 2016.

less common. Spikes in electricity prices will disappear (Dougherty). There won't be as many noisy power plants. Fewer ugly oil rigs will dot the landscape. And Californians will be proud that their state is leading the way in protecting the planet.

So who favors using solar energy? The honest answer is, "most people." Solar energy enjoys a broad base of support.

For example, solar energy is championed by scientists. More than a dozen professors, engineers, and academics participated in the study cited above. They stated that the "main goal" of American solar policy should be "a massive scale-up of solar generation" (Schmalensee xi).

Neil deGrasse Tyson, a world-famous astrophysicist, agrees. Tyson describes the sun as "a nearby source of essentially unlimited energy" (McCue). It is downright senseless to not use that energy.

Solar power is also popular with business leaders. Tesla's Elon Musk is known for being forward-thinking. He recently described how "a little corner of Nevada or Utah" could soon "power the entire United States" (Harrington). Perhaps Musk and other business owners will take notice when California's public buildings use solar energy. Perhaps they will be inspired. Perhaps they will start to use solar power for their companies' electric needs, too.

Lastly, the general public supports solar power. Harvard University professor Stephen Ansolabehere did a study on public attitudes toward renewable energy. The study lasted twelve years. It was very thorough. In the end, he described solar power as "hugely popular, overwhelmingly popular." His study found that 90 percent of Americans want to see the use of solar energy and wind energy rise (McMahon).

The benefits are clear. Scientific experts and captains of industry concur. John and Jane Q. Public are on board. And with the cost of creating electricity with solar panels down more than 60 percent over the last eight years, the price is right ("A Renewable Energy Boom"). The time to act is now.

California is a hub of creativity. It is a cradle of innovation. The state is home to the fantastic films of Hollywood. It is home to the cutting-edge companies of Silicon Valley. Imagination and progress are part of the state's DNA. They are at the core of its identity.

Today, California can again show its imagination. It can again prove its commitment to progress. It can do something that is both smart and moral. It can continue to lead.

The state can provide electricity to all of its public buildings with solar power. Indeed, it must do so. And when it does, the state will give a deeper meaning to its most famous nickname: Sunny California.

A "farm" of solar panels at Furnace Creek, California, in Death Valley National Park

Sources

"A Renewable Energy Boom." *The New York Times*, 4 Apr. 2016, p. A18.

"Benefits of Renewable Energy Use." *Union of Concerned Scientists*, 8 Apr. 2013, www.ucsusa.org/clean-energy/renewable-energy/public-benefits-of-renewable-power#.Wfduv3rXr7o.

Dougherty, Elizabeth. "The High Cost of Summer Energy Price Spikes." *Federal Relations RSS*, Boston University, 9 June 2017, www.bu.edu/federal/2017/06/09/the-high-cost-of-summer-energy-price-spikes/.

Harrington, Rebecca. "Elon Musk just made an incredibly important point about solar energy." *Business Insider*, Business Insider, 15 Dec. 2015, www.businessinsider.com/elon-musk-solar-panels-to-power-the-earth-2015-12.

McCue, Dan. "Astrophysicist Neil deGrasse Tyson tackles renewable energy's future." *Renewable Energy Magazine*, Dan McCue, 27 June 2011, www.renewableenergymagazine.com/interviews/astrophysicist-neil-degrasse-tyson-nbsp-tackles-renewable.

McMahon, Jeff. "Americans Want America To Run On Solar and Wind." *Forbes*, 1 Jan. 2015, www.forbes.com.

Morton, Oliver. "Solar energy: Silicon Valley sunrise." *Nature*, vol. 443, no. 7107, July 2006, pp. 19–22.

"QuickFacts." *U.S. Census Bureau.* Selected for California, www.census.gov/quickfacts/CA.

Schmalensee, Richard, and Vladimir Bulovic. *The Future of Solar Energy: An Interdisciplinary MIT Study*, Massachusetts Institute of Technology, energy.mit.edu/wp-content/uploads/2015/05/MITEI-The-Future-of-Solar-Energy.pdf.

Walsh, Jim. "California's Solar Battle: Fossil Fuels vs. Solar Power." *Food & Water Watch*, 23 Mar. 2017, www.foodandwaterwatch.org.

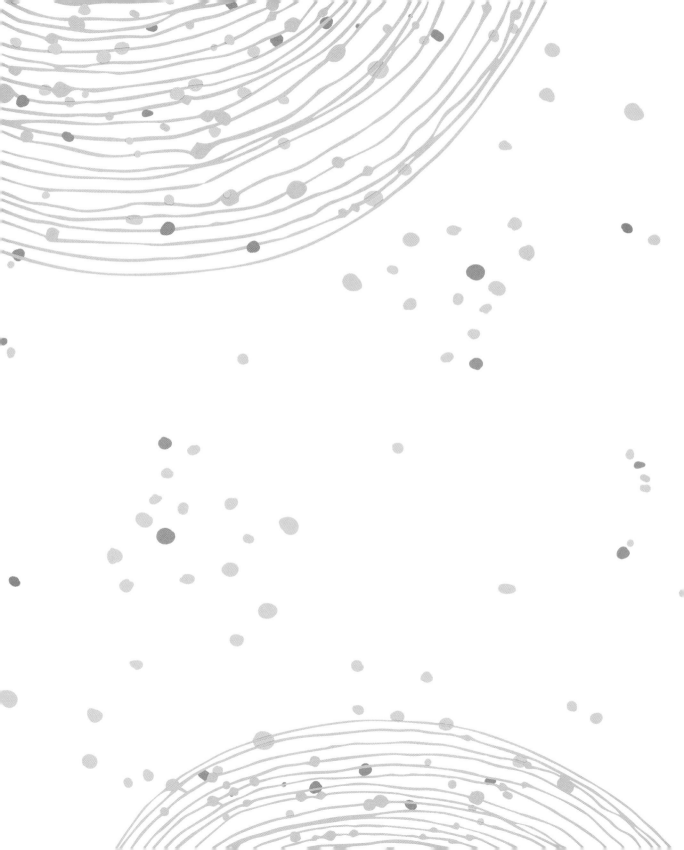

Solar-Powered Public Buildings?
Not So Fast, California!

For many, the idea of solar power is like a dream. It's exciting. It's modern. It's hugely popular. In fact, a Harvard professor conducted a 12-year study on how the public viewed solar energy. He found that 9 out of 10 people want the use of solar energy to rise (McMahon).

"Imagine," these folks say, "never paying another electricity bill."

"We can make power without making pollution," they cry.

"The sun can meet all our energy needs," they shout.

Now these people argue for using solar energy to power California's public buildings. They want places like city halls, government offices, and courthouses to run on solar electricity. They think libraries, police stations, and schools should go solar, too.

And, sure, it sounds like a good idea. After all, who doesn't want to save money? Who doesn't want to protect

A solar farm near Los Angeles

the planet? Who rejects the use of advanced technology? It all seems so simple.

But reality is rarely simple. Using solar power is much more complicated than it seems. The facts are complex. And the plans to use solar electricity in California's public buildings are full of **pitfalls** and problems.

For one thing, this is no small task. There are thousands and thousands of public buildings in

....

pitfalls hidden traps or not easily recognized dangers

California. Providing electricity to all of them through solar power will be expensive. How expensive? Even if every building could run on a small 10 kilowatt solar panel system—and most cannot—the move to solar power would cost between $22,000 and $29,000 per building (Matasci). Do the math. That adds up to millions of dollars in installation costs alone. And that is a very low estimate.

Further, the estimate does not include the cost of rewiring old buildings. It does not factor in the expenses that come with updating them to handle new technology. In some cases, roofs will need to be replaced so they can support solar panels. In others, trees will have to be cut down so they don't keep the sunlight from reaching the panels. These are all real costs. And they will have to be paid before a single light bulb in a single public building is lit by solar electricity.

The picture begins to look even less rosy when one learns more about solar power.

Right now, California generates quite a bit of solar electricity. In March of 2017, there were days when 40 percent of the state's electricity came from solar energy (Franz). That may sound great, but it is not. Because that is actually more solar electricity than the state can handle.

Excess solar electricity can overload power lines. Overloaded power lines lead to power blackouts. Blackouts are inconvenient for people and harmful to businesses. They must be avoided. So on days when the state makes too much solar electricity, California must deliver much of that power to neighboring states.

If that does not sound great, just wait. It gets worse.

When California makes too much solar power, the state does not just give that electricity to its neighbors. It does not simply present Arizona or Nevada or Oregon with power at no charge. The state does not say, "Here you go, neighbor! Enjoy some free electricity!"

Rather, California actually pays those other states to take its extra solar electricity (Penn). That's right. California—and Californians—give other states money to take the solar electricity that California—and

Electrical power lines and utility towers against a sunset outside Los Angeles

Californians—paid to create. Getting rid of excess power costs the state more cash!

Imagine that situation playing out on a personal level. You go to the store. You spend $50 on peas. Then you come home, steam all those peas, and realize that you made a mistake. You bought too many peas. You cannot possibly eat them all before they spoil.

But you can't just give the extra peas to your neighbor. She won't let you. Instead, you have to pay your neighbor $10 to take them off your hands. Now you're costing yourself more and saving your neighbor money. Meanwhile, she doesn't have to buy her own peas. She can just eat yours.

That is what California does with its solar electricity. Except California's mistake does not cost $60. California's mistake costs millions.

So why would a state that already makes more solar power than it can use increase production further? Does California like paying other states to take its electricity? Is there any sense to such behavior?

Of course not. The *New York Times* notes that, already, California's "per-unit [energy] prices are among the highest in the nation." The use of renewable energy sources like solar and wind power are part of the reason why. These sources "have added between 3 percent and 5 percent to the cost of energy" (Gardiner). The state does not need to make matters worse by adding even more to its power bill.

It is time to be realistic about the dream of using solar power. It's time to wake up. Admit that powering California's public buildings with solar energy will be too expensive. Acknowledge that the state already makes more solar electricity than it can use. Accept that just because an idea is popular does not also make it good.

Works Cited

Franz, Julia. "California's electrical grid can't handle all the solar energy the state is producing." *Public Radio International*, 20 July 2017, www.pri.org/stories/2017-07-20/california-s-electrical-grid-can-t-handle-all-solar-energy-state-producing.

Gardiner, Beth. "California Leads a Quiet Revolution." *The New York Times*, 6 Oct. 2015.

Matasci, Sara. "2017 Average Cost of Solar Panels in the U.S. | EnergySage." *EnergySage Solar News Feed*, EnergySage, 13 Oct. 2017, news.energysage.com/how-much-does-the-average-solar-panel-installation-cost-in-the-u-s/.

McMahon, Jeff. "Americans Want America To Run On Solar and Wind." *Forbes*, 1 Jan. 2015, www.forbes.com.

Penn, Ivan. "California invested heavily in solar power. Now there's so much that other states are sometimes paid to take it." *The Los Angeles Times*, 22 June 2017, www.latimes.com/projects/la-fi-electricity-solar/.

Meet a Supreme Court Justice

Opening Statement to the Senate Judiciary Committee

by Sonia Sotomayor

13 July 2009

Thank you, Mr. Chairman. I also want to thank Senators Schumer and Gillibrand for their kind introductions.

In recent weeks, I have had the privilege and pleasure of meeting eighty-nine senators, including all the members of this committee. Each of you has been gracious to me, and I have so much enjoyed meeting you. Our meetings have given me an illuminating tour of the fifty states and invaluable insights into the American people.

There are countless family members and friends who have done so much over the years to make this day possible. I am deeply appreciative for their love and support. I want to make one special note of thanks to my mother. I am here, as many of you have noted, because of her aspirations and sacrifices for both my brother Juan and me.

Judge Sonia Sotomayor at her Senate confirmation hearing

I am very grateful to the president and humbled to be here today as a nominee to the United States Supreme Court.

The progression of my life has been uniquely American. My parents left Puerto Rico during World War II. I grew up in modest circumstances in a Bronx housing project. My father, a factory worker with a third grade education, passed away when I was nine years old. On her own, my mother raised my brother and me. She taught us that the key to success in America is a good education. And she set the example, studying alongside my brother and me at our kitchen table so that she could become a registered nurse.

We worked hard. I poured myself into my studies at Cardinal Spellman High School, earning scholarships to Princeton University and then Yale Law School, while my brother went on to medical school. Our achievements are due to the values that we learned as children, and they have continued to guide my life's endeavors. I try to pass on this legacy by serving as a mentor and friend to my many godchildren and to students of all backgrounds.

Over the past three decades, I have seen our judicial system from a number of different perspectives: as a big-city prosecutor, as a corporate litigator, as a trial judge, and as an appellate judge. My first job after law school was as an assistant district attorney in New York. There, I saw children exploited and abused. I felt the pain and suffering of families torn apart by the needless death of loved ones. I saw and learned the tough job law enforcement has in protecting the public. In my next legal job, I focused on commercial, instead of criminal, matters. I litigated issues on behalf of national and international businesses and advised them on matters ranging from contracts to trademarks.

My career as an advocate ended—and my career as a judge began—when I was appointed by President George H.W. Bush to the United States District Court for the Southern District of New York. As a trial judge, I did decide over 450 cases, and presided over dozens of trials, with perhaps my most famous case being the Major League Baseball strike in 1995.

After six extraordinary years on the district court, I was appointed by President Clinton to the United States Court of Appeals for the Second Circuit. On that court, I have enjoyed the benefit of sharing ideas and perspectives with wonderful colleagues as we have worked together to resolve the issues before us.

I have now served as an appellate judge for over a decade, deciding a wide range of constitutional, statutory, and other legal questions. Throughout my seventeen years on the bench, I have witnessed the human consequences of my decisions. Those decisions have not been made to serve the interests of any one litigant, but always to serve the larger interest of impartial justice.

In the past month, many senators have asked me about my judicial philosophy. Simple: fidelity to the law. The task of a judge is not to make law; it is to apply the law. And it is clear, I believe, that my record in two courts reflects my rigorous commitment to interpreting the Constitution according to its terms; interpreting statutes according to their terms, and Congress's intent; and hewing faithfully to precedents established by the Supreme Court and by my circuit court. In each case I have heard, I have applied the law to the facts at hand.

The process of judging is enhanced when the arguments and concerns of the parties to the litigation are understood and acknowledged. That is why I generally structure my opinions by setting out what the law requires and then explaining why a contrary position, sympathetic or not, is accepted or rejected. That is how I seek to strengthen both the rule of law and faith in the impartiality of our judicial system. My personal and professional experiences help me to listen and understand—with the law always commanding the result in every case.

Since President Obama announced my nomination in May, I have received letters from people all over this country. Many tell a unique story of hope in spite of struggles. Each letter has deeply touched me. Each reflects a dream, a belief in the dream that led my parents to come to New York all those years ago. It is our Constitution that makes that dream possible, and I now seek the honor of upholding the Constitution as a justice on the Supreme Court.

Senators, I look forward in the next few days to answering your questions, to having the American people learn more about me, and to being part of a process that reflects the greatness of our Constitution and of our nation.

Thank you all.

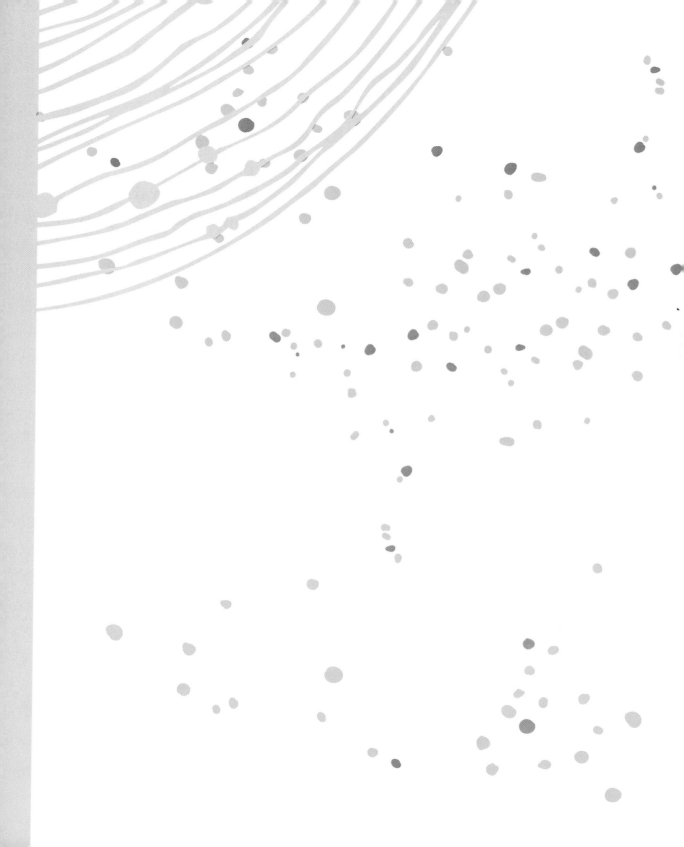

Sherlock Holmes

The Red-Headed League

by Sir Arthur Conan Doyle

I visited my friend, Mr. Sherlock Holmes, one day in the autumn of last year. I found him in deep conversation with a very stout, elderly gentleman with fiery red hair. I apologized for my intrusion and was about to leave, but Holmes abruptly pulled me into the room and closed the door behind me.

"You could not possibly have come at a better time, my dear Watson," he said. "I'd like you to meet Mr. Jabez Wilson." Sherlock Holmes turned to the red-haired man. "Dr. Watson has been my partner in many of my most successful cases, and I have no doubt that he will be a great help to me in yours also. Please, tell your story again."

The stout gentleman rose from his chair and gave a **bob** of greeting. He pulled a dirty, wrinkled newspaper from the inside pocket of his coat.

....

bob a quick up-down motion, not a bow

I took a good look at the man. I tried, just as Holmes would, to learn something about him from his dress or appearance.

I did not gain much from my inspection. Our visitor seemed an average British tradesman. There was nothing remarkable about the man except his blazing red head.

Sherlock Holmes noticed me eyeing our visitor, and he smiled at my questioning glance. "My dear Watson," he said, "beyond the obvious facts that he has at some time done manual labor, that he has been in China, that he has done much writing lately, I can deduce nothing else."

Mr. Jabez Wilson started in his chair. "How in the name of good fortune did you know all that, Mr. Holmes? How did you know I did manual labor? It's true, I began as a ship's carpenter."

"Your hands, my dear sir," said Holmes. "Your right hand is quite a size larger than your left. You have worked with it, and the muscles are more developed."

"Ah, of course, I forgot that. But the writing?"

"Your right cuff is very shiny for five inches, and the left has a smooth patch near the elbow where you rest it upon the desk."

"Well, yes," said Mr. Jabez Wilson. "But how did you know I've been to China?"

"The fish that you have tattooed above your right wrist could only have been done in China," said Holmes. "I have made a small study of tattoo marks and have even written a bit on the subject. The delicate pink of the fishes' scales is quite peculiar to China. In addition, I see a Chinese coin hanging from your watch chain. Now, Mr. Wilson, if you would tell us about your situation."

"Well, it is just as I have been telling you, Mr. Holmes," said Jabez Wilson, mopping his forehead. "I have a small business at Saxe-Coburg Square, near London. It's not very large, and lately it has only just given me a living. I used to be able to keep two assistants, but now I can only keep one. And it would be hard even to pay him, but he is willing to work for half wages, to learn the business."

"You seem most fortunate to have an employee willing to work for half wages," said Sherlock Holmes. "It is not a common experience these days. What is the name of this youth?"

"His name is Vincent Spaulding, and he's not such a youth, either. It's hard to say his age. I don't think I could find a smarter assistant, Mr. Holmes. I know very well that he could earn twice what I am able to give him. But if he is satisfied, why should I put ideas in his head?"

"Why, indeed? He is still with you, I presume?"

"Yes, sir. He and a girl who does a bit of cooking and cleaning. That's all I have in the house, for I am a widower and never had any family. We live very quietly, sir. But then, Spaulding, he came down into my office just this day eight weeks ago, with this very paper in his hand, and he says, 'Mr. Wilson, I wish that I was a red-headed man. Look at this.' And he handed me this paper. Here, read it for yourself."

I took the paper from him and read the following advertisement:

TO THE RED-HEADED LEAGUE:

There is now a vacancy open which will pay a member of the League four pounds a week for light work. All red-headed men are eligible. Apply in person on Monday, at eleven o'clock, to Duncan Ross, at the offices of the League, 7 Pope's Court, Fleet Street.

"What on earth does this mean?" I cried.

Holmes chuckled and wriggled in his chair, as was his habit when in high spirits. "It is a little off the beaten track, isn't it? Very good. Now, Mr. Wilson."

"Of course, my hair is red," Jabez Wilson began. "Spaulding thought that I might be chosen for the vacancy. He even offered to come down with me. So we shut the business up, and started off for Fleet Street.

"I have never seen such a sight, Mr. Holmes. From north, south, east, and west every man who had a shade of red in his hair had tramped into the City to answer the advertisement. Fleet Street was choked with red-headed folk. Every shade of color they were—straw, lemon, orange, brick, Irish setter, liver, clay. But, as Spaulding said, there were not many who had my real, vivid, flame-colored tint.

"When I saw how many were waiting, I would have given up, but Spaulding would not hear of it. He pushed and pulled and butted until he got me through the crowd, and right up to the office steps. Two lines of people stood on the stairs, some going up in hope, and some coming back dejected. But we wedged in as well as we could, and soon found ourselves in the office.

"'This is Mr. Jabez Wilson,' Spaulding said to the manager, Duncan Ross, 'and he is willing to fill a vacancy in the League.'

"Mr. Ross, he gazed at my hair until I felt quite

bashful. Then suddenly he plunged forward, shook my hand, and congratulated me warmly on my success. 'I cannot recall when I have seen anything so fine,' he said. Then Mr. Ross stepped over to the window and shouted through it at the top of his voice that the vacancy was filled. A groan of disappointment came up from below, and the folk all trooped away in different directions, until there was not a red head to be seen in the square.

"Mr. Ross told me that to earn the four pounds a week, I must stay in the office from ten to two every day, copying out the Encyclopedia Britannica. I thought it strange, but I agreed, and for eight weeks, I copied the books. Every morning I was there at ten, and every afternoon I left at two. And for eight weeks, I received four golden sovereigns for my work. But this morning, I went to the office, and found a sign on the door that said:

> ### THE RED-HEADED LEAGUE IS DISSOLVED.
> #### Oct. 9, 1890.

"I went round to the offices, but no one had ever heard of the Red-Headed League or Mr. Duncan Ross. I did not wish to lose such a place without a struggle, and so," concluded Jabez Wilson, "as I had heard that you give advice to poor folk who need it, I came right away to you."

"And you did very wisely," said Holmes. "Your case is remarkable. I shall be happy to look into it. From what you have told me, I think graver problems hang from it than might at first sight appear. Tell me, what is he like, this assistant of yours who first called your attention to the advertisement, this Vincent Spaulding?"

"Small, stout-built, very quick in his ways, no hair on his face, around thirty years old. Has a white splash of acid on his forehead."

Holmes sat up in his chair. "I thought as much," said he. "Have you ever observed that his ears are pierced for earrings?"

"Yes, sir. He told me that a gypsy had done it for him when he was a lad."

"Hum!" said Holmes, sinking back, deep in thought. "And he has cared well for your business while you were away?"

"Nothing to complain of, sir. Though he does have his faults," said Mr. Wilson. "Never was such a fellow for photography. Snapping away with a camera when he ought to be learning, then diving down into the cellar like a rabbit into its hole to develop his pictures. That is his main fault; but, on the whole, he's a good worker."

Holmes nodded. "Mr. Wilson," he said, "today is Saturday. I hope that by Monday we will have solved your case."

"Well, Watson," said Holmes, when our visitor had left us, "let us go to Saxe-Coburg Square."

2

Holmes and I traveled by the Underground as far as
Aldersgate, and a short walk took us to Saxe-Coburg
Square. Four lines of dingy, two-storied brick houses
looked out over a lawn of weedy grass. A brown board
with *Jabez Wilson* in white letters announced the place
where our red-headed client had his business. Sherlock
Holmes stopped in front of it with his head to one side,
and looked it all over, his eyes shining brightly. He
thumped vigorously upon the pavement with his stick
two or three times, then went up to the door and knocked.
A bright-looking, clean-shaven young fellow opened it,
and asked him to step in.

"Thank you," said Holmes, "I only wished to ask you how you would go from here to the Strand."

"Third right, fourth left," answered the assistant promptly, closing the door.

"Smart fellow, that," observed Holmes as we walked away. "I have known something of him before."

"Yes," said I, "Mr. Wilson's assistant seems to play a large part in this mystery of the Red-Headed League. I am sure that you knocked so that you might see him."

"Not him."

"What then?"

"The knees of his trousers."

"And what did you see?"

"What I expected to see."

"Why did you beat the pavement?"

"My dear doctor, this is a time for observation, not for talk. We are spies in an enemy's country. We know something of Saxe-Coburg Square. Let us now explore what lies behind it."

The road in which we found ourselves as we turned the corner was as different as the front of a painting is to the back. The street was one of the busiest in all of London.

"Let me see," said Holmes, standing at the corner, and glancing along the line, "I should like to remember the order of the houses here. There is Mortimer's, the tobacconist; the little newspaper stand, the Coburg branch of the City and Suburban Bank, the Vegetarian Restaurant, and McFarlane's carriage-building shop. That carries us right on to the next block. And now, doctor, we've done our work, so it's time we had some play—a sandwich, a cup of coffee, and then off to hear the violin at St. James Hall, where all is sweetness and harmony. You want to go home, no doubt."

"Yes, it would be as well."

"And I have some errands which will take some hours. This business at Saxe-Coburg Square is serious."

"Why serious?"

"A considerable crime is afoot. But I have every reason to believe that we shall be in time to stop it. I shall want your help tonight."

"At what time?"

"Ten will be early enough."

"I shall be at Baker Street at ten."

"Very well. And, I say, doctor! There may be some little danger, so kindly put your army revolver in your pocket." He waved his hand, turned on his heel, and disappeared in an instant among the crowd.

I trust that I am not a dense man. I had heard what Holmes had heard, and seen what he had seen. Yet he already knew what had happened and what was going to happen, while to me, the business was as mysterious as ever. I tried to puzzle it out, but gave up, and set the matter aside until night should bring an explanation.

It was a quarter-past nine when I started from home and made my way to Baker Street. On entering Holmes's room, I found him talking with two men, one of whom was Peter Jones, the official police agent. The other was a long, thin, sad-faced man, with a very shiny hat.

"Ha! Our party is complete," said Holmes, buttoning up his pea-jacket, and taking his heavy hunting crop from the rack. "Watson, I think you know Mr. Jones, of Scotland Yard? Let me introduce you to Mr. Merryweather, who is to be our companion in tonight's adventure."

"I hope a wild goose may not prove to be the end of our chase," observed Mr. Merryweather gloomily.

"Mr. Merryweather," said Sherlock Holmes, "I think you will find the hunt worth your while tonight. I hope that I may have the pleasure of introducing you to John Clay, murderer and thief. Tonight he will try to steal no less than thirty thousand pounds from your bank. Now, gentlemen, it is past ten, and quite time that we started. If you two will take the first cab, Watson and I will follow in the second."

Sherlock Holmes said little during the long drive. As we rattled through the gas-lit streets, he lay back in the cab, humming the tunes he had heard in the afternoon.

"We are close now," my friend remarked. "This fellow Merryweather is a bank director, so he has a personal interest in the matter. And I thought it well to have Jones with us. He is incompetent, though he is brave as a bulldog and stubborn as a lobster if he gets his claws on anyone. Here we are, and they are waiting for us."

We had reached the street Holmes and I had visited in the morning. Mr. Merryweather unlocked the door to the City and Suburban bank. He led us down through endless tunnels and gates, until we came to the bank's cellar. We entered a huge vault, piled all round with crates and boxes.

"You are not very vulnerable from above," Holmes remarked, as he held up the lantern and gazed about him.

"Nor from below," said Mr. Merryweather, striking his stick upon the stones that lined the floor. "Why, dear me, it sounds quite hollow!" he remarked, looking up in surprise.

"I must really ask you to be a little more quiet!" said Holmes severely. "You might have just put our expedition in terrible danger. Might I ask that you sit on one of those boxes and not interfere?"

Mr. Merryweather perched upon a crate, with an injured expression on his face. Holmes fell upon his knees on the floor and, with the lantern and a magnifying glass, began to examine the cracks between the stones. After a few seconds, he sprang to his feet and put his glass in his pocket.

"We are at present, Doctor," he said, "in the cellar of the City branch of one of the main banks of London. The crate upon which Mr. Merryweather sits contains more than 2,000 gold pieces, not to mention these many other crates, all filled with gold. So you see, there are reasons why the more daring criminals of London should take an interest in this cellar. And I expect that within hours matters will come to a head. These are daring men, and they may do us some harm unless we are careful. I shall stand behind this crate. You conceal yourselves behind those. Then, when I flash a light upon them, close in swiftly."

We put out the lantern and took up our positions in the thick darkness of the vault. After waiting what seemed like hours, suddenly my eyes caught the glint of a light.

With a rending, tearing sound, one of the broad white stones in the floor turned over, and left a square, gaping hole, through which streamed the light of a lantern. A clean-cut, boyish face peeped out, looked around, then drew himself up out of the hole. He turned and began to haul out another man, nimble and small like himself, who had a pale face and a shock of very red hair.

"It's all clear," the first man whispered. "Have you the chisel and the bags? Great Scott! Jump, Archie, jump, and I'll swing for it!"

Sherlock Holmes had sprung out and seized the man by the collar. The other dived down the hole, and I heard the sound of tearing cloth as Jones clutched at his pant leg. The light flashed upon the barrel of a revolver, but Holmes's hunting crop came down on the man's wrist, and the pistol clinked upon the stone floor.

"It's no use, John Clay," said Holmes blandly. "You have no chance at all."

"So I see," the other answered coolly. "I fancy that my pal is all right, though I see you have got his coat-tails."

"Inspector Jones has three men waiting for him at the door," said Holmes.

"Oh, indeed? You seem to have thought of everything. I must compliment you."

"And I you," Holmes answered. "Your red-headed idea was very clever."

John Clay smiled. Then Jones clapped the handcuffs on him and led him away.

Later that night, Holmes explained. "You see, Watson, it was perfectly obvious to me that the Red-Headed League and copying the Encyclopedia were only a way to get Mr. Wilson out of his shop for several hours each day. The two rogues put the advertisement in the newspaper. One lures Mr. Wilson to the League, the other pretends to be the manager. From Mr. Wilson's description, I knew the assistant was one of the most daring criminals in London."

"But how could you guess what the men wanted?"

"The man's business was a small one, so they could not want to steal from him. It must then be something out of the house, but what? I thought of the assistant's fondness for photography, and his trick of vanishing into the cellar. The cellar! He was doing something in the cellar—something which took many hours a day for months on end. I could think of nothing except that he was digging a tunnel to some other building.

"When we visited the square, I beat upon the pavement with my stick to see if the cellar stretched out in front of the building or behind. It was not in front. When I rang the bell, I saw that the assistant's pant-knees were worn and stained, from hours of digging. When we walked round the corner, I saw that the bank was behind Mr. Wilson's shop, and I knew I had solved the problem. I called Scotland Yard and Mr. Merryweather, and the rest you saw yourself."

"But how did you know that they would make their attempt tonight?" I asked.

"Well, when they closed the League office, that was a sign that they cared no longer about Mr. Jabez Wilson's presence. In other words, they had completed their tunnel. But they had to use it soon, or it might be discovered. Saturday would suit them better than any other day, as it would give them two days before the bank opened and anyone noticed the money was missing."

"You reasoned it out beautifully," I exclaimed, admiringly. "It is so long a chain, and yet every link rings true."

"It saved me from boredom," he answered, yawning.

The Adventure of the Blue Carbuncle

by Sir Arthur Conan Doyle

I called upon my friend, Sherlock Holmes, on the second morning after Christmas, to wish him a happy holiday. He was lounging upon the sofa in a purple dressing gown among a pile of crumpled morning newspapers. He was peering through a magnifying glass at an old, shabby black hat, cracked in several places.

"Am I interrupting you?" I asked.

"Not at all. I am glad to have a friend with whom I can discuss my findings."

I sat down in his armchair and warmed my hands before his crackling fire. A sharp frost had set in, and the windows were thick with the ice crystals. "I suppose," I remarked, "that, homely as it looks, that hat has some deadly story linked on to it. Is it the clue that will guide you to the solution of a mystery, or the punishment of a crime?"

"No, no. No crime," said Sherlock Holmes, laughing. "Only one of those odd little events that happen when you have four million people crowded together within the space of a few square miles. You know Peterson, the **commissionaire**?"

"Yes."

"This trophy belongs to him."

"Oh, it is his hat?"

"No, no, he found it. No one knows who the owner is. Watson, don't look at it as just a battered billycock. Instead, see it as an interesting problem.

"Peterson brought it here on Christmas morning, along with a good fat goose. The facts are these: about four o'clock on Christmas morning, Peterson, a very honest fellow, was coming home from a holiday party. In front of him, he saw a tall man, carrying a white goose over his shoulder. As the man reached the corner of Goodge Street, a group of roughs attacked him. One knocked off his hat. So the man raised his stick to defend himself. But when he swung the stick over his head, he accidentally smashed the shop window behind him.

---

commissionaire chiefly Brisitish, a uniformed attendant such as a messenger or porter

"Peterson had rushed forward to protect the stranger from his attackers. But the man, shocked at having broken the window, and seeing an official-looking person in uniform running towards him, dropped his goose and took to his heels. The roughs also ran away. And so Peterson was left with this battered hat and a marvelous Christmas goose."

"Which Peterson surely returned to the man?" I asked.

"My dear fellow, there lies the problem. 'For Mrs. Henry Baker' was printed upon a small card which was tied to the bird's left leg. You can see the initials 'H. B.' upon the lining of this hat. But there are hundreds of Henry Bakers in this city of ours. It will not be easy to return the hat and the goose to the right man."

"What, then, did Peterson do?"

"Peterson knows that even the smallest problems interest me, so he brought me the goose and the hat. The goose had to be eaten before it spoiled, so he took it home. I, of course, have the man's hat. And I would like to return it to him, along with his Christmas dinner."

"How on earth will you figure out who he is? Not from his hat!"

"Precisely so."

"But you are joking. What can you gather from this old battered felt?"

"Here is my magnifying glass. You know my methods.

What can you find out yourself about the man who has worn this hat?"

I took the tattered object in my hands and turned it over. It was a very ordinary black hat of the usual round shape, though much the worse for wear. The lining had been of red silk, but was now spotted and stained. There was no maker's name, but, as Holmes had remarked, the initials "H. B." were written on one side. For the rest, it was cracked, very dusty, and worn in several places, though it appeared that the owner had smeared the worn patches with ink to hide them.

"I can see nothing," said I, handing it back to my friend.

"On the contrary, Watson, you can see everything, but you fail to reason from what you see. You are too timid in drawing your inferences."

"Please tell me, what can you infer from this hat?"

Holmes picked up the hat and gazed at it. "Obviously, this man was fairly well-to-do within the last three years. But he has now fallen upon hard times. That may be why his wife is angry with him."

"My dear Holmes!"

"Still, he cares what people think of him. He mostly stays at home, and he is out of shape. He has **grizzled** hair, which he has had cut within the last few days, and which he smoothes with lime-cream."

"You are certainly joking, Holmes."

"Not in the least. Is it possible that you do not see how I reached these conclusions?"

"I must confess that I am unable to follow you."

"This hat is three years old. These flat brims curled at the edge were fashionable then. It is a hat of the very best quality. If this man could afford to buy such an expensive hat three years ago, and has had no new hat since, then he has certainly gone down in the world."

"Well, that is clear enough," I said. "But what about

grizzled streaked with gray

the rest: that he stays at home, is out of shape, has grizzled hair that has been recently cut, and that he uses lime-cream?"

"All of that you can see when you look through a magnifying glass. Look, there are a number of hair-ends, clean cut by a barber's scissors. They're quite sticky, and the whole hat smells of lime-cream. This dust is not the gritty, gray dust of the street but the fluffy brown dust of the house, showing that it has been hung up indoors most of the time. The marks of moisture upon the inside are proof positive that the wearer perspires a lot while walking, so he is probably not in good shape."

"But his wife—you said that she was angry with him."

"This hat has not been brushed for weeks. My dear Watson, when you have a week's worth of dust upon your hat, and when your wife allows you to go out that way, I will fear that you also will have made her quite upset."

"But he might be a bachelor."

"No, remember the card on the bird's leg, which said 'For Mrs. Henry Baker.' He was bringing home the goose as a peace offering to his wife."

"You're very clever," said I, laughing. "But no crime has been committed. No harm has been done except the loss of a goose and an old hat. All of this seems to be rather a waste of energy."

As Sherlock Holmes opened his mouth to reply, the door flew open, and Peterson, the commissionaire, rushed into the apartment. His cheeks were flushed and he was dazed with astonishment.

"The goose, Mr. Holmes! The goose!" he gasped.

"What of it? By the looks of you, it must have gotten up from its platter and flapped off through the window."

"No, see here, sir! See what my wife found in its crop!" Peterson opened his hand and showed a sparkling blue stone. It was smaller than a bean, but so brilliant that it twinkled like a star in the dark hollow of his hand.

Sherlock Holmes sat up with a whistle. "Peterson, that is a treasure indeed. Do you know what you have there?"

"A diamond, sir? A precious stone?"

"It's more than *a* precious stone. It is *the* precious stone."

"Not the Countess of Morcar's blue **carbuncle**!" I cried.

"Precisely so," said Holmes.

"It was stolen just a few days ago, wasn't it?" I asked.

"Precisely so, on December 22nd, just five days ago," replied Holmes. "John Horner, a plumber, was accused

---

carbuncle a precious stone cut in a convex but not faceted way

of having stolen it from the Countess's jewel-case. I have some articles about it here, I believe." Holmes rummaged among his newspapers. At last, he smoothed one out and read:

HOTEL COSMOPOLITAN JEWEL ROBBERY

John Horner, 26, plumber, was arrested on the charge of having stolen from the Countess of Morcar the valuable gem known as the blue carbuncle.

James Ryder, head attendant at the hotel, said that he had shown Horner to the Countess's dressing room on the day of the robbery to fix a pipe. He stayed with Horner for a while, but then was called away.

When Ryder returned, he found that Horner had disappeared and that the bureau had been forced open. Also, a small case in which the Countess kept her jewel was lying empty upon the dressing table.

Ryder called the police. Horner was arrested that evening, but the stone was not found on him or at his home. The arresting officer reported that Horner struggled frantically and strongly declared his innocence.

At the court hearing, evidence was given that the prisoner had been previously convicted of robbery. Horner, who was greatly upset, fainted away and was carried out of court.

"Hum! So much for the police," said Holmes thoughtfully. "The question for us is, how did the Countess's blue carbuncle travel from her jewelry-case to Mr. Henry Baker's Christmas goose? Let us try the simplest way first. We will advertise in the evening newspapers. If this fails, we will have to try another method. Please pass me a pencil and that slip of paper, Watson. Now, then:

Found at the corner of Goodge Street, a goose and a black felt hat. Mr. Henry Baker can have them by coming to 221B Baker Street at 6:30 this evening.

"That is very clear," I said. "But will Mr. Baker see it?"

"Well, he is sure to keep an eye on the papers, since, to a poor man, the loss was a heavy one. Everyone to whom he told the story will see his name in the ad and show it to him. Here you are, Peterson, run down to the newspapers and have this ad put in tonight."

"Very well, sir. And the stone?"

"Ah, yes, I will keep the stone. Thank you. And, I say, Peterson, please buy a goose on your way back and leave it here with me. We must have one to give to this gentleman in place of the one your family is now enjoying."

After Peterson left, Holmes took up the stone and held it against the light. "It's a pretty thing," said he. "See how it glitters and sparkles. Of course it is a magnet for crime. This tiny piece of crystallized charcoal has already been the object of several robberies and murders. Who would think that so pretty a toy would send men to prison? I'll lock it up in my strong-box and send a message to the Countess to say that we have it."

"Holmes," I asked, "do you think that the plumber, Horner, is innocent?"

"I'm not sure."

"Well, then, do you think Henry Baker had anything to do with the crime?"

"I think Henry Baker is absolutely innocent. He probably has no idea that the bird he carried was more valuable than a goose made of solid gold. But I will know that when the man answers the advertisement."

"And you can do nothing until then?"

"Nothing."

"In that case I shall return to my patients. But I shall come back at 6:30. For I should like to see the solution to this tangled case."

"Very glad to see you. I dine at seven. There is a turkey, I believe. But before she starts cooking, perhaps I ought to ask Mrs. Hudson to examine the bird's crop."

It was a little after half-past six when I returned to Baker Street. As I neared the house, I saw a tall man waiting outside Holmes's door. Just as I arrived the door was opened, and we were shown up together to Holmes's rooms.

"Mr. Henry Baker, I believe," said Holmes, rising from his armchair. "Please take this seat by the fire. It is a cold night. Ah, Watson, you have just come at the right time. Now, Mr. Baker, is this your hat?"

"Yes, sir, it certainly is." Henry Baker ran his hand through his grizzled hair. I noticed the scent of lime-cream.

"We kept these things for some days," said Holmes, "because we expected to see an advertisement from you giving your address. Why didn't you advertise?"

Our visitor laughed sheepishly. "Shillings are not so plentiful with me as they once were. I thought that the gang of roughs who attacked me had carried off both my hat and the bird. I thought it would be a waste of money to try to get them back."

"Of course. By the way, about the bird, we had to eat it."

"To eat it!" Our visitor half rose from his chair in his excitement.

"Yes, it would have spoiled if we hadn't. But here is

another goose. It is about the same weight and perfectly fresh. Will it do?"

"Oh, certainly, certainly," answered Mr. Baker, sighing with relief.

"Of course, we still have the feathers, legs, crop, and so on of your own bird, so if you wish—"

The man burst into a hearty laugh. "They might be useful as souvenirs of my adventure," he said, "but beyond that, they are of no use to me."

Sherlock Holmes glanced sharply at me with a slight shrug of his shoulders.

"There is your hat, then, and there is your bird," he said. "By the way, would you tell me where you got the other one? I have never seen a better goose."

"Certainly, sir," said Baker, tucking the goose under his arm. "I bought it from a man named Windigate at the Alpha Inn." He clapped his hat upon his head, thanked us, and went off upon his way.

"So much for Mr. Henry Baker," said Holmes when he had closed the door behind him. "He knows nothing about the jewel. But would you like to follow up on his clue while it is still hot?"

"By all means," I replied.

We trudged through the snow to the Alpha Inn. Holmes walked to the bar and ordered two glasses of ale from the ruddy-faced, white-aproned landlord.

"Your ale should be excellent if it is as good as your geese," said he.

"My geese?" The man seemed surprised.

"Yes. I just spoke to Mr. Henry Baker. He said he'd bought his goose from you."

"Ah! Yes, I see. Sorry, sir, but them's not our geese."

"Indeed! Whose are they, then?"

"Well, I got the two dozen from a salesman in Covent Garden."

"Indeed? I know some of them. Who was it?"

"Breckinridge is his name."

"Ah! I don't know him. Well, here's to your good health, landlord, and prosperity to your house. Good-night."

As we came out into the frosty air, Holmes buttoned his coat and said, "Now for Mr. Breckinridge. Remember, Watson, even though we have only a goose at this end of the chain, at the other end, there is a man who will spend years in prison unless we can prove that he is innocent."

Holmes and I hurried to Covent Garden Market. One of the largest stalls had the name *Breckinridge* written on it. The salesman was helping a boy put up the shutters.

"Good-evening. Sold out of geese, I see," said Holmes, pointing at the bare slabs of marble. "Fine birds they were, too. Where did you get them from?"

To my surprise, the salesman was suddenly furious.

"Now, then, mister, what do you want? Let's have it straight, now."

"It's straight enough. I want to know who sold you your geese."

"Well then, I won't tell you. So now!"

"Oh, it's not important. But why are you so upset over such a small thing?"

"Upset? You'd be upset, too, if you were as pestered as I am. When I pay good money for a good goose, that should be the end of the business. But all day long, it's been 'Where are the geese?' and 'Who did you sell the geese to?' and 'What will you take for the geese?' You'd think they were the only geese in the world, to hear the fuss that's been made over them."

"Well, I don't know who else has been asking," said Holmes casually. "If you won't tell us, the bet is off, that's all. But I'm always ready to back my opinion on a matter of geese, and I have a fiver on it that the bird I ate is country bred."

"Well, then, you've lost your fiver, for it's town bred," snapped the salesman.

"It's nothing of the kind."

"I say it is."

"I don't believe it."

"D'you think you know more about geese than I, who have handled them ever since I was a nipper? I tell you, those birds were town bred."

"You'll never persuade me to believe that."

"Will you bet, then?" asked the salesman.

"It would be taking your money, because I know I'm right. But I'll bet a sovereign, just to teach you not to be so obstinate."

The salesman snorted. "Bring me the book, Bill," he said.

The boy brought out a great, greasy volume. He laid it beneath the lamp.

"Now then, Mr. Know-It-All," said the salesman, "You see this book?"

"Well?"

"That's the list of the folk from whom I buy. D'you see? Well, then, here on this page are the country folk I buy from. Now, then! You see this other page in red ink? Well, that is a list of my town suppliers. Now, look at that third name. Just read it out to me."

"Mrs. Oakshott, 117 Brixton Road—egg and poultry supplier," read Holmes.

"Quite so. Now, read the last entry."

"'December 22nd. Twenty-four geese at 7 shillings.'"

"Quite so. There you are. And underneath?"

"'Sold to Mr. Windigate of the Alpha Inn, at 12 shillings.'"

"What have you to say now, Mr. Know-It-All?"

Sherlock Holmes drew a sovereign from his pocket and threw it down upon the slab. He turned away as though he was disgusted. But a few yards off, he stopped under a lamppost and laughed in his hearty, silent way.

"When you see a man with a horse-racing form sticking out of his pocket, you can always get him to talk with a bet," said he, chuckling.

Just then, a loud hubbub broke out from the stall that we had just left. Turning round we saw Breckinridge shaking his fist at a little rat-faced fellow.

"I've had enough of you and your geese!" Breckinridge shouted. "If you come pestering me again, I'll set the dog at you!"

"Ha! This may save us a visit to Brixton Road,"

whispered Holmes. "Come with me. Let's see who this fellow is." Holmes strode through the crowd, and touched the little man on the shoulder. The man jumped and turned around, his face pale.

"You will excuse me," said Holmes blandly, "but I could not help overhearing your conversation with the salesman. Perhaps I can help you."

"Who are you?" asked the man in a quavering voice. "How could you know anything of the matter?"

"My name is Sherlock Holmes. It is my business to know what other people don't know."

"But you can know nothing of this!"

"Excuse me, I know everything about it. You are trying to trace a goose sold by Mrs. Oakshott, of Brixton Road, to a salesman named Breckinridge, by him in turn to Mr. Windigate, of the Alpha, and by him to Mr. Henry Baker."

"Oh, sir, you're just the man I am looking for!" cried the little fellow, almost in tears.

"Of course. But please tell me who it is that I have the pleasure of helping."

The man paused for a moment. "My name is John Robinson," he answered with a sly glance.

"No, your real name," said Holmes sweetly. "It is always awkward doing business with a false one."

The stranger blushed. "Well then," said he, "my real name is James Ryder."

Sherlock Holmes hailed a cab. "Precisely so—the head attendant at the Hotel Cosmopolitan. Please step into the cab, and I shall soon be able to tell you everything you wish to know."

In a half-hour we were back at Baker Street.

"Here we are!" said Holmes cheerily as we filed into his rooms. "Now, then! You want to know what became of a white goose with a black bar across the tail?"

Ryder trembled. "Oh, sir," he cried, "can you tell me where it went to?"

"It came here."

"Here?"

"Yes, and it was a most amazing bird. I'm not surprised that you want to find it. You know, it laid an egg after it was dead—the prettiest, brightest little blue egg ever seen."

Holmes unlocked his strong-box and held up the blue carbuncle, which shone out like a star. Ryder's eyes bulged with fear.

"The game's up, Ryder," said Holmes quietly. "You had heard of the Countess's blue carbuncle, had you not?"

"Her maid told me about it," Ryder said in a crackling voice.

"I see. Well, the temptation of sudden wealth was too

much for you. But you were not very careful in the means you used. You knew that this man Horner, the plumber, had been convicted of robbery before. So, you damaged the pipes in the Countess's room, then sent for Horner. When the gem was stolen, you knew that everyone would suspect him. After he left, you cracked open the jewel-case, raised the alarm, and had the poor man arrested."

Ryder threw himself down on the rug and clutched at Holmes's knees. "Have mercy!" he shrieked. "Think of my parents! It would break their hearts. I never went wrong before! I never will again. I swear it. I'll swear it on a Bible. Oh, don't bring it into court! Please!"

"Get back into your chair!" said Holmes sternly. "It is very well to cringe and crawl now. But you thought little enough of this poor Horner being punished for a crime he did not commit."

"I will go away, Mr. Holmes. I will leave the country. Then the charge against him will break down."

"Hum! We will talk about that. Now let us hear the true story of how the stone got into the goose and how the goose got to market. Tell us the truth, for that is your only hope of safety."

"I will tell you what happened, sir," said he. "When Horner was arrested, I knew I had to get away with the stone at once. I did not know if the police would search

THE ADVENTURE OF THE BLUE CARBUNCLE

me and my room, too. The hotel wasn't safe, so I went to my sister's house. She and her husband, a man named Oakshott, raise geese for market."

Ryder passed his tongue over his parched lips and then continued. "I have a friend who was once a thief. I knew that if I took the stone to him, he would show me how to sell the stone for money. But the police could stop me and search me at any time. How could I keep the jewel safe?

"I remembered that my sister told me I might have my pick of her geese for a Christmas present. So I went into the goose yard, and caught a big white bird with a barred tail. I pried its bill open and thrust the stone into its throat. The bird gulped, and I felt the stone pass into its crop. Then it broke loose and fluttered off among the others.

"I told my sister which goose I wanted. She said I could take it with me. So I caught it and took it to my friend. But when we cut open the goose, my heart turned to water. There was no sign of the stone.

"I rushed back to my sister's and hurried into the yard. But there was not a bird to be seen. She told me they had all gone to Breckinridge at Covent Garden. I asked her if there was another with a barred tail. She said yes, and that they were so alike she herself couldn't tell them apart.

"Well, I ran to this man Breckinridge, but he'd sold them all. You know the rest. My sister thinks that I am going mad. If only she knew! I think I might be. Now I am myself a thief, and I never even touched the wealth for which I sold my character." He burst into sobs, and buried his face in his hands.

There was a long silence, broken only by Sherlock Holmes tapping his fingertips on the table. Suddenly, my friend rose and threw open the door.

"Get out!" he said.

"What, sir? Oh, Heaven bless you!"

"No more words. Get out!"

No more words were needed. There was a rush, a clatter upon the stairs, the bang of a door, and the crisp rattle of running footfalls from the street.

"After all, Watson," said Holmes, "Horner is not in danger. Ryder will not speak against him, and the stone will be returned, so the case will fall apart. Perhaps I am committing a crime, but perhaps I am saving a soul. This fellow will not go wrong again. He is too frightened. If we send him to jail now, we will make him a jail-bird for life."

He reached for his clay pipe. "Besides," he concluded, "it is the season of forgiveness. Chance sent us a most entertaining problem, and solving it has been its own reward. Now, Doctor, if you will join me, we will begin another investigation, in which also a bird will be the most delicious object."

The Adventure of the Three Students

A Dramatic Adaptation in Three Short Acts

Characters

SHERLOCK HOLMES, 40, a detective
DR. JOHN WATSON, 42, Holmes's assistant
MR. HILTON SOAMES, 55, a professor of Greek
BANNISTER, 63, Soames's butler
GILES GILCHRIST, 20, a college student
DAULAT RAS, 19, a college student
MILES MCLAREN, 20, a college student

Stage

At center, a desk and a chair both face downstage. Slightly to their left and upstage is a window along the back wall. There is a small table under the window with another chair next to it. This is the office of a professor at Pembroke College, Oxford University, circa 1895.

To the right of the desk is a doorframe—the door inside it open—that leads to the professor's bedroom. The bedroom also has a window along the back wall, though this one is obscured by large hanging curtains. The foot of a bed can be seen at the far right, upstage.

At right, far downstage, are two comfortable chairs that face one another.

Act I

Lights up. At rise, Sherlock Holmes and Dr. Watson sit in the two chairs downstage right. Watson's legs are crossed and he reads a book. Holmes also has a book in his hand, but he promptly closes it. His left leg bounces with nervous energy as his eyes scan this way and that. He readjusts himself in his seat, opens the book momentarily, and then closes it again with some agitation. The noise captures the attention of Dr. Watson, who looks up from his reading.

WATSON: Having a relaxing evening?

HOLMES: Very funny, Watson. You know I can't stand to be away from London for this long.

Watson checks his pocket watch.

WATSON: We've been gone for precisely 21 hours.

HOLMES: Quite long enough, if you ask me.

WATSON: Here I shall remind you that you were the one who said you needed to come to Oxford to do some research.

HOLMES: Indeed. And the sooner I can finish it, the better. I've never been quite so dreadfully bored in all my life.

WATSON: No offense taken.

HOLMES: Oh, come now, Watson. You know I wasn't talking about your company. It's just that these university towns are calm, so tame.

WATSON: Many people enjoy university towns for that exact reason.

HOLMES: I am not many people.

WATSON: That much is certain.

There is the sound of a knock at a door offstage.

HOLMES: Come in! And please bring with you some kind of excitement.

Mr. Soames now enters from right. He is a tall man with wild hair and a nervous energy that keeps him in near-constant motion. Watson and Holmes both stand to greet him.

SOAMES: I beg your pardon, Mr. Holmes. Dr. Watson, perhaps you remember me? Professor Hilton Soames.

Watson and Soames shake hands.

WATSON: Of course, Professor Soames. Good to see you, again. Holmes, Professor Soames and I knew one another in the army.

SOAMES: Many years ago. I heard today from the librarian that you and Mr. Holmes were in town to do some research. And I realize now how lucky I am to have you both here in Oxford at this moment.

HOLMES: And why is that, Professor?

SOAMES: Because, Mr. Holmes, I need your help.

HOLMES: My help?

SOAMES: Yes. You see, there's been a rather painful incident at Pembroke College this afternoon, and I'm not sure what to do. Your expertise is well-known, and I thought I might beg you to use your talents to help solve a mystery.

HOLMES: If a crime has been committed, call the police. I am only in Oxford for a few days, and I really desire no distractions.

SOAMES: I understand, Mr. Holmes. Honestly, I do. But I'm afraid I cannot call the police, for no crime has been committed yet. Further, bringing the police into the matter can only lead to scandal.

Holmes cocks his head to the side, intrigued. He sits again and crosses his legs.

HOLMES: Scandal, you say? Well, congratulations, Professor, you've captured my interest. Please tell me how I might help.

SOAMES: Oh, thank you, Mr. Holmes. I shall tell you as briefly as possible. Please feel free to interrupt—

HOLMES: To ask questions as needed. Yes, yes. Please begin.

SOAMES: Yes, very well. First, I must explain that my subject is Greek, and I am giving a big exam tomorrow. The student who scores highest on the exam will win the Fortescue scholarship.

WATSON: Very prestigious.

SOAMES: And very valuable. The student who wins it will have next year's tuition entirely paid by the Fortescue Foundation.

HOLMES: Quite generous.

SOAMES: Yes, and a major part of the exam involves the students translating a long passage from Homer's Iliad. Indeed, the passage I selected takes up the first three sheets of the exam. Of course, no one knows which passage I've chosen until they receive the test—

HOLMES: So that no one can prepare in advance. Thus you must strive to keep hidden the three pages of the exam on which the passage is printed.

SOAMES: You understand precisely.

HOLMES: Continue.

SOAMES: Well, this afternoon, I left those pages with

the passage on them rolled up on my desk. Yet this evening, when I returned to my office, I found those three pages unrolled and separated, lying in differing places in the room, one on the floor, one on the table under the window, one on my desk where I'd left it.

WATSON: Did anyone else have access to the room while you were away?

SOAMES: Only my servant, Bannister, who has looked after my room for ten years. He has always proven to be a good and honest man, and I trust him entirely.

HOLMES: Had he been in your office while you were out?

SOAMES: He had, but only briefly. He entered around five o'clock to ask if I wanted tea. When he saw I wasn't there, he left immediately.

WATSON: And you know this because you already spoke to him about this incident?

SOAMES: Yes, he was the first person I called upon when I discovered the papers strewn about my office.

HOLMES: And how did Bannister, the honest and trustworthy servant, react when you told him that the exam papers had been tampered with?

SOAMES: He nearly fainted. He collapsed in a chair, and I left to get him some water.

HOLMES: I see. Did you find any other clues, Professor?

SOAMES: Yes, a few. On the table by my window were several shreds from a sharpened pencil and a broken tip of lead. Apparently the culprit copied the passage so quickly that he broke his pencil point and had to sharpen it.

HOLMES: (*Smiling*) Our cheater was in a hurry. An excellent observation, Professor.

SOAMES: Thank you, Mr. Holmes. Also, the table by the window has a fine surface of red leather. It was smooth and unstained this morning. But now it has a cut in it about three inches long.

HOLMES: Wonderful.

SOAMES: Finally, on that same table, I found a small ball of black dough or clay with specks of something that looks like sawdust. I don't know what it is, but I know it must have come into my office with whomever copied the papers.

HOLMES: Fantastic. Professor Soames, you have done me a great service.

SOAMES: I have?

HOLMES: Yes. You have relieved me of the crippling boredom brought by my brief stay in this dreadfully dull town. And so, to repay you, I shall look to solve this mystery quickly and discreetly.

SOAMES: Oh, thank you, Mr. Holmes.

Holmes stands again.

HOLMES: Dr. Watson, what say you and I go have a look at the scene of the crime?

WATSON: Let's go.

All three exit right. Lights down.

Act II

Lights up. Soames, Holmes, and Watson enter the office from left. Holmes takes a moment to look around. He examines the desk and chair first. Then he walks over to the window to look at the table and chair there and stare out through the glass. He picks something up off the table.

SOAMES: Do you see the rip in the table there, Mr. Holmes?

HOLMES: I do, Professor. And this is the black dough or clay that you spoke of earlier?

Holmes holds something up in his hand.

SOAMES: That's it.

HOLMES: There's another piece of it here under the chair.

Holmes reaches down and picks up a second clump of clay from the floor. He pockets both.

HOLMES: How high is this window from the ground?

SOAMES: Six feet. But it has long been painted shut. No one could have opened it to gain access to my office.

HOLMES: I see. And did anyone visit your office and see the papers on the desk? Before you left and they were disturbed, I mean.

SOAMES: Yes, there are three students whose rooms are above me in this building. One of them, a young man named Daulat Ras, stopped by this morning to ask what time the examination began.

WATSON: And might he have seen the papers then?

SOAMES: Maybe, but they were rolled up. He could not have known that they contained the passage that would appear on the exam.

HOLMES: Perhaps, but he may have suspected. After all, I don't see any other papers rolled up on your desk.

SOAMES: That's true.

HOLMES: So it's possible that, seeing the only rolled up papers in your office, he suspected that they were confidential. Using logic, he may have reasoned that, with the test coming up tomorrow, the rolled up papers contained part of the exam.

SOAMES: I suppose you're right. My goodness, the rumors of your towering intellect were not exaggerated.

HOLMES: There will be ample time for flattering me and my intellect later, Professor. Right now I'm interested in your servant, Bannister. Did he know that the rolled up papers contained the passage for the exam?

SOAMES: No, I'm the only one who knew...

HOLMES: You said when you told him, he felt faint and sat in a chair. Which chair?

SOAMES: That one near the window.

HOLMES: I see. Well, what happened is quite clear. The guilty party came in, took the papers, sheet by sheet, from your desk. He brought them to this table by the window. That way, he could keep watch. If you approached across the courtyard outside, he would see you and could then escape.

SOAMES: Except that would not have worked. For I entered from the other side of the building. He would not have been able to see me from that window.

HOLMES: Ah, that's good! So he copied what he could while you were gone, keeping a lookout, but then had to retreat fast when he heard you opening the door. That's why he didn't have time to place the papers back on your desk.

WATSON: Or clean up his pencil shavings or the pencil point.

HOLMES: Exactly. Professor, you didn't see anyone in the office when you entered, correct?

SOAMES: Correct.

HOLMES: (*Pointing to the bedroom doorway*) And this doorway...

SOAMES: Leads to my bedroom. But there is no way out of the bedroom except through the office.

HOLMES: Interesting. There is no window in the bedroom?

SOAMES: There is, but it is also painted closed.

WATSON: So how could the cheater have escaped?

HOLMES: Patience, Watson. We're getting there. Professor, when you came in and saw the papers had been moved, what did you do?

SOAMES: I called Bannister, and he came immediately.

HOLMES: Your servant, yes. You said he came in and felt faint.

SOAMES: Correct. He had to sit down, he was so upset.

HOLMES: And you left to get him some water.

SOAMES: That's right.

HOLMES: Would you mind getting this Bannister now?

SOAMES: Certainly.

HOLMES: And do you mind if I take a look around your bedroom?

SOAMES: Not at all. I will be back in a moment.

Soames exits left. Holmes, followed by Watson, enters the bedroom. He looks around.

WATSON: Not much to it, is there?

HOLMES: No, it's a very small room. The bed is too low to hide under. And there is no closet, just a chest of drawers.

WATSON: Anyone hiding in here would have just one option.

HOLMES: Precisely. Behind the curtains.

Now Holmes moves one of the curtains in front of the bedroom window to the side. Something on the ground catches his eye, and he bends over.

HOLMES: Hello, what's this?

He picks something up from the ground and holds it up for Watson to see.

WATSON: Another lump of clay. And it's got a tiny hole in the middle of it.

HOLMES: A keen eye, Watson. I believe we are getting closer.

Holmes pockets the lump of clay. Soames reenters from left, trailed by Bannister, who is short and bald. He is also as white as a sheet and sweating so much that he must occasionally dab his forehead with a handkerchief. Holmes and Watson reenter the office from the bedroom.

HOLMES: Mr. Bannister, I presume.

Bannister nods.

HOLMES: I'm Sherlock Holmes. This is my associate, Dr. Watson. May I ask you a few questions?

Bannister nods again.

HOLMES: Professor Soames tells me that, when he told you that someone had broken into his office and tampered with the examination papers, you grew faint. Is that correct?

Bannister nods a third time.

HOLMES: And you had to sit down. And please don't simply nod again. Did you have to sit down right away?

BANNISTER: I did, sir. I feared that I was going to lose consciousness.

HOLMES: So you were near where you are now, and you went to the chair. Which chair? The one at the desk or the one by the window?

BANNISTER: The one by the window, sir.

HOLMES: That's peculiar.

BANNISTER: Sir?

HOLMES: The chair at the desk is closer. You felt faint, bypassed the nearest chair, and made your way clear across the room to the chair by the window. Any idea why?

BANNISTER: No, sir. I didn't care which chair I sat in. Wasn't even thinking about it, to be honest. Perhaps I just zeroed in on that one by the window.

Holmes nods. He paces. He strokes his chin. Bannister dabs his forehead.

HOLMES: There's no need to be so nervous, Bannister. Professor Soames has vouched for your honesty and decency.

BANNISTER: (*To Soames*) Thank you, sir.

HOLMES: Professor Soames also mentioned that three students live in the building in rooms above this one. He named one Daulat Ras. Who are the other two?

BANNISTER: One is named Giles Gilchrist and the other is called Miles McLaren.

HOLMES: And what can you tell me about them?

BANNISTER: Giles Gilchrist is an excellent scholar and an athlete. Tall and strong.

HOLMES: How tall?

BANNISTER: Taller than you by five or six inches, I'd say.

HOLMES: And I'm six feet tall. Very good. Continue.

BANNISTER: He competes on the college track and field team in the hurdles and the long jump. He is a fine fellow. His father was Sir Jabez Gilchrist, who lost all the family's money betting on horses when Giles was just ten. So Giles was left very poor, but he is hardworking and industrious.

HOLMES: Very good. And the other fellow? McLaren?

BANNISTER: McLaren is a little fellow with glasses and red hair. I know Professor Soames considers him to be one of the brightest students in Pembroke College.

SOAMES: Quite true. Though he lacks principles. He was nearly expelled after being accused of cheating in his first year. It could not be proven, though, so he remained. He has done little work most of the term, and he's seemed rather worried about the exam. He has quite a temper, as well.

HOLMES: Interesting. And the third fellow? Daulat Ras? What kind of student is he?

SOAMES: Steady and methodical. Though Greek is his worst subject.

HOLMES: Very good. Thank you, gentlemen. Now, if it's not too much trouble, I would very much like to see these three students. Could you perhaps summon them to meet us here in an hour?

BANNISTER: Certainly, sir.

Bannister and Soames exit left. Watson turns to look at Holmes, who stares out the window.

WATSON: You've nearly solved the case, haven't you?

HOLMES: Perhaps. But I think a quick walk across campus for some fresh air will help me think more clearly. Come! We must be back here in an hour.

Now Holmes and Watson exit left, as well. Lights down.

Act III

Lights up. Professor Soames and Bannister stand by the office window. Near the desk stand the three students: Giles Gilchrist, lean and quite tall, has his hands in his pockets and his head down; Miles McLaren, nearly a foot shorter than Gilchrist, red-haired and wearing glasses, paces angrily; Daulat Ras, the shortest of the three, reads to himself from a book and checks his watch. Now Holmes and Watson enter from the left. Everyone turns their attention to them.

HOLMES: Gentlemen, I thank you for coming to speak to me. (*Pointing to each student*) Mr. Gilchrist, Mr. McLaren, and Mr. Ras?

The students all nod.

HOLMES: I'm Sherlock Holmes; this is my colleague, Dr. Watson.

WATSON: (*Tipping his hat*) Lads, good evening.

SOAMES: Mr. Holmes and Dr. Watson have agreed to assist me in a most important matter.

HOLMES: That's correct. Has Professor Soames told you why I want to speak to you all?

MCLAREN: He has not, and I must say that I resent the interruption to my evening, Mr. Helms!

HOLMES: Holmes.

MCLAREN: Whatever your name is! Are you aware that we have a very important exam tomorrow?

HOLMES: I am.

MCLAREN: And do you know what people tend to do the evening before an exam?

HOLMES: Study?

MCLAREN: Correct! So what do you think I was doing when I was summoned down here to speak with you?

HOLMES: Logic suggests that you were studying.

MCLAREN: Bravo, Mr. Holmes. Your logic has served you well. I was studying. But I had to stop. So, if it's all the same to you, I would very much like to get whatever this is over with so I can return to my studying.

Holmes smiles. A moment passes.

HOLMES: Thank you, Mr. McLaren. You may return to your studying.

This catches McLaren off guard. He waits a moment. Holmes nods toward the entrance to the office, and McLaren hurriedly exits left.

HOLMES: And Mr. Ras, I see that you have not let our meeting interrupt your studies at all.

Ras looks up from his book.

RAS: I'm sorry, Mr. Holmes. The exam tomorrow is for a scholarship, and I want very much to win it. It will be a huge relief to not have to pay tuition next year.

HOLMES: I quite understand, Mr. Ras. And I wish you luck on the exam. You may return to your room to continue studying, as well.

Ras is also surprised by this abrupt dismissal, but he closes his book and exits left. Now Gilchrist, the only remaining student, begins to pace slowly.

WATSON: I'm not quite sure I understand, Holmes. You've dismissed those two without hardly questioning them at all.

HOLMES: My dear Watson, I didn't ask them here to question them. I simply needed to see them. And now that I have, I am confident in the conclusion that I have drawn. Mr. Gilchrist, why don't you have a seat.

Gilchrist nods and sits by the desk.

HOLMES: Mr. Bannister, what was in the chair by the window this afternoon?

Gilchrist shoots a look at Bannister. Bannister gulps.

BANNISTER: Sir?

HOLMES: I think you heard me, Bannister. What was in the chair?

BANNISTER: I-I don't think…

GILCHRIST: My gloves.

HOLMES: Your gloves. Of course. You took them off so you could copy the passage, but you forgot to grab them when you had to go hide.

Gilchrist nods sadly.

SOAMES: Sorry, I'm not following entirely. So it was you, Mr. Gilchrist, who broke into my office this afternoon?

GILCHRIST: Yes, sir, I'm terribly sorry. I was just so tempted and I couldn't resist.

SOAMES: But…how…

HOLMES: How did he do it? As I said earlier, anyone who saw the rolled up papers on the desk could have logically assumed that they were part of the exam since they were the only sheets that you made the effort to conceal.

WATSON: But Mr. Gilchrist didn't come into the office. How could he have seen them?

HOLMES: He didn't need to come into the office to see them. Mr. Gilchrist is quite a bit bigger than me, and I stand six feet tall. The same height as…

WATSON: The office window. That's why you wanted to

see all three students to make sure Gilchrist was the only one tall enough to see through the window.

HOLMES: Very good, Watson. You're catching on. Mr. Gilchrist is tall enough to have seen the rolled up papers through the window, realized that Professor Soames was out, and entered.

SOAMES: Then he began to copy the sheets by the window so he could keep a look out.

HOLMES: But since you came back to the building from a different direction, he didn't see you approach. When he heard you turn the doorknob, he had no choice but to hide in the bedroom.

WATSON: Behind the curtains.

HOLMES: The only place to hide, which is why we found a lump of clay there that matches the lump of clay that Professor Soames found on the table by the window.

SOAMES: I see. But what was that clay?

Gilchrist puts his head in his hands.

HOLMES: Dr. Watson can tell you, I think.

Watson looks at Holmes. He shakes his head.

WATSON: I'm afraid I cannot say what the clay was, Holmes.

HOLMES: Oh, Watson. Will you ever begin to pay attention to the world around you? We just went on a walk across campus. Do you recall that?

WATSON: Of course.

HOLMES: And what did we pass on that walk?

WATSON: The library. The dining hall. The athletic fields. The—

HOLMES: Stop right there. What did we see at the athletic fields?

WATSON: The running track. Grass. The long jump pit— the long jump pit!

HOLMES: Yes. What about it, Watson?

WATSON: Why, it was filled with the same type of dark clay that we found here in the office.

HOLMES: Exactly. Earlier, Mr. Bannister told us that Mr. Gilchrist competes on the college track and field team. I contend now that he was returning from practice in his athletic spikes this afternoon when he saw the opportunity to copy the exam passage.

WATSON: And when he came in, he tracked some of the clay from the long jump pit that had gotten stuck on his spikes.

HOLMES: Precisely. When he recognized that, he took off his shoes, placing them on the side table there.

SOAMES: But when he heard me open the door and had to dash into the bedroom to hide, he quickly grabbed the spikes and one of their points made a tear in the leather.

HOLMES: Look at the two detectives at work. Now just one question remains.

WATSON: What's that, Holmes?

HOLMES: Why did Mr. Bannister try to cover for Mr. Gilchrist?

All eyes turn to Bannister. For the first time, he stands up tall and does not pat his head with his handkerchief. He speaks calmly and confidently.

BANNISTER: Because I have known him his whole life.

SOAMES: What's that now, Bannister? His whole life? He's only been at college for two years.

GILCHRIST: But Mr. Bannister worked for my family for decades. He was with us until I was ten, when my father gambled away all of our money and we could no longer afford to pay him.

BANNISTER: So when Professor Soames summoned me after he realized that someone had broken into his office, I came in and immediately saw Mr. Gilchrist's gloves on that chair.

HOLMES: Then, recognizing the gloves, you pretended to feel faint so you could sit on them and hide them from Professor Soames.

BANNISTER: Correct. I didn't know what else to do. In that moment, I panicked. I couldn't bear the thought of Mr. Gilchrist being expelled if he was caught. You must understand, I was there the night he was born. I remember him learning to walk, learning to read. I helped teach him to ride a bicycle.

HOLMES: So you sat on the gloves, and when Professor Soames went to get you some water...

GILCHRIST: He returned the gloves to me and told me to get out of the room.

HOLMES: You are a loyal man, Mr. Bannister.

GILCHRIST: And an honest and good one. He came to me earlier tonight and said that I must own up to my actions. I must take responsibility. And he's right. So I've made a decision.

Gilchrist stands now.

BANNISTER: What have you decided, Mr. Gilchrist?

GILCHRIST: I have decided to leave the university. I intend to join the police force in London.

HOLMES: An interesting decision. Why the police, Mr. Gilchrist?

GILCHRIST: I feel that joining the police will allow me to do some good in the world and earn an honest living. Also, I hope that, since I have not followed through on my rash decision to cheat on Professor Soames's exam, I will not have my reputation tarnished as a result of my actions.

HOLMES: Well, Mr. Gilchrist, I appreciate your confession. Mr. Bannister, I respect your loyalty and your decency. Professor Soames, I trust you are satisfied that this matter is resolved.

SOAMES: Quite. Thank you, Mr. Holmes.

HOLMES: It was my pleasure. Now, Dr. Watson, let us return to our rooms so that we can finish our business in Oxford and return to London as soon as possible.

WATSON: I'm right behind you, Holmes.

Holmes and Watson start to leave, but Holmes stops briefly and turns to Gilchrist.

HOLMES: One more thing, Mr. Gilchrist. I wish you luck. I trust that a bright future awaits you in London, and perhaps our paths will cross again once you join the police force. Until then, remember this moment. You have fallen low, but I hope to see in the future that you have risen high again.

Holmes and Watson exit. Lights down.

End of play.

Text Credits

Text from *Young Frederick Douglass: The Slave Who Learned to Read* © 1994 by Linda Walvoord Girard. Original illustrations by Colin Bootman. Adapted and reillustrated by permission of Albert Whitman & Company. All rights reserved.

"Run, Kate Shelley, Run" by Julia Pferdehirt, copyright © 1999 by Julia Pferdehirt. Reprinted by permission of the author.

Text from *Clara Barton: Founder of the American Red Cross* by Augusta Stevenson. Copyright © 1946, 1962 by the Bobbs-Merrill Company, Inc. Reprinted with the permission of Simon & Schuster Books for Young Readers, an imprint of Simon & Schuster Children's Publishing Division. All rights reserved.

Text from *Will Clark: Boy Adventurer* by Katharine E. Wilkie. Copyright © 1963 The Bobbs-Merrill Company. Copyright © renewed 1991 by Katharine E. Wilkie. Reprinted with the permission of Aladdin, an imprint of Simon & Schuster Children's Publishing Division. All rights reserved.